5.95

P9-DWR-865

THE PHYSIOLOGY
OF FLOWERING

These Studies are designed to inform the mature student—the undergraduate upperclassman and the beginning graduate student—of the outstanding advances made in various areas of modern biology. The books will not be treatises but rather will briefly summarize significant information in a given field and interpret it in terms of our current knowledge of the rapidly expanding research findings within the life sciences. Also it is hoped that the Studies will be of interest to teachers and research workers.

BIOLOGY ⟵
STUDIES

William S. Hillman
Yale University

THE PHYSIOLOGY
OF FLOWERING

Holt, Rinehart
and Winston

New York • *Chicago* • *San Francisco*
Toronto • *London*

MARCH, 1964

23637-0112

PRINTED IN THE UNITED STATES OF AMERICA

preface ▶▶▶▶▶

To the botanist flowering is of interest as the means of sexual reproduction in the higher plants, and because the processes leading to it provide experimental systems for the study of environmental and internal controls of development—problems of basic significance throughout biology. To the rest of mankind, which often has more pressing problems to consider, flowering is nevertheless of the greatest practical importance since agriculture is based on the control of flowering and its resultant fruits and seeds. Flowering has been studied with both attitudes for many centuries; only during the past few decades, however, has a large body of knowledge about flowering been accumulated. It is the purpose of this book to survey this knowledge. The major emphasis, which simply reflects the direction of most research, will be on processes affecting the initiation and early development of flowers rather than on associated or subsequent events. Historical details are omitted except when they are required to clarify current concepts.

I have tried to write for several kinds of readers, from graduate students in botany and other branches of biology to laymen with some formal training in science. Inevitably, then, any given reader will find some passages too elementary or others insufficiently explained. As for the relatively small group of professional plant physiologists who specialize in the study of flowering, I hope this book will serve as a useful review for them. They should not expect to find much new in it, except perhaps another point of view, and there are as many of these as there are specialists.

This question of point of view, particularly in presentation, has not been an easy one to resolve. There is much to be said for the practice of sketching the broad lines of a topic with a few intellectually satisfying concepts and not burdening the student immediately with exceptions and difficulties. If I have avoided this procedure—and surely the bewildered reader of Chapter Five will agree that I have—it is because I am afraid it can be fundamentally misleading. My intention is to introduce the reader to the field and if possible to give him the "feel" of it, bringing him close to the position of the research workers themselves. Since in my opinion science progresses, like all endeavors, by fumbling, backing out of dead ends, and now and then taking a few steps forward, it is often easy to believe in a clear pattern of conceptually clean "breakthroughs" after some time has passed, but it is harder to do so as the work becomes more recent. Or, at least, I doubt my own ability at this sort of judgment. The alternative, then, is to stress the phenomena, the empirical observations; these are not so likely to be subjectively distorted, and it is these that must be lived with, examined, correlated, and finally understood.

All this is of course no excuse for a mere random collection of "facts," and the reader will find nothing of the kind. It is, however, the justification for bringing in exceptions almost simultaneously with the tentative rules, for employing an often deliberate vagueness in terminology—since words used in a systematic, authoritative way can often conceal ignorance—and for stressing, above all, the kinds of experiments and results rather than merely the concepts they may or may not illustrate. I can think of no better way to convey the extreme openness of the subject, the way in which few if any principles are irrevocably established. It is all a question of how much confusion is necessary to provide a true picture of the present state of things; I have tried to avoid an excess, but not to exclude it entirely.

A general outline of the way in which I have grouped various topics for consideration is provided by the table of contents, and requires no further comment here. However, some remarks on the bibliography and the manner in which papers are cited may be useful.

The proportion of general reviews to original experimental articles cited is relatively high, and I have made no attempt to include all the relevant literature. Frequently a paper is considered not because it is the first or most important of its kind but simply because it provides a particularly good example of a problem under discussion. The great preponderance of English-language references is simply a concession to the convenience of both reader and writer, and does not reflect the frequency or importance of publications in other languages. Fortunately for the English-speaking world most of the work from other countries is reviewed, and much is even reported, in English by the original workers themselves.

I have adopted the following convention with regard to citations in the text. If a statement is followed simply by author (s) and date, for example, Hamner (1940), the paper cited has original data on the point in question. Directions to *see* a paper, on the other hand, indicate reviews or other discussions from which further references may be obtained. All plants are referred to for the first time by both common (if any) and scientific names. Thereafter, the practice adopted is arbitrary, but the index can always be used to establish one from the other.

In summary, I have tried to treat the field in a manner not quite like that to be expected from a technical review or article, but in such a way that the previously uninformed reader will afterward be able to read any of these with understanding and enjoyment; and then, best of all, perhaps try his own hand at the game.

W. S. H.

New Haven, Connecticut
September, 1961

acknowledgments

During the time this book was written, the author was supported entirely by research grants from the National Science Foundation.

The patient cooperation of Violet Esdaile and Margaret Wark in typing successive stages of the manuscript has been of great value.

Discussions and correspondence with numerous investigators have contributed greatly to this survey, but particular thanks are due Dr. Bruce A. Bonner and Dr. Ian M. Sussex for critically reading the manuscript.

contents

Extreme modification of development by photoperiodism in the common weed *Chenopodium rubrum. Right,* a plant germinated and grown under 8-hour photoperiods; much of the bulk of the 3-week-old seedling consists of flower parts. *Left,* a plant germinated and grown under 20-hour photoperiods; after more than 3 months, it remains completely vegetative. (Right-hand photograph from Cumming [1959], by permission of the editors of *Nature;* both photographs courtesy of Dr. B. G. Cumming of the Canada Department of Agriculture.)

chapter one

Background

Experimental work is the main concern of this study, but some purely descriptive information on flowering should be helpful. This chapter considers, first, the structure and origin of flowers as dealt with by morphologists. The natural history of certain flowering habits will then be briefly described, and an outline of some of the methods used to "measure" or evaluate flowering concludes the chapter.

MORPHOLOGY OF FLOWERING

The word "flower" is commonly used for structures of the greatest variety, from those of the elm, simple and inconspicuous, to the showy, complex blossoms of orchids or sunflowers. Morphologists use the term "flower" to mean a determinate sporogenous shoot bearing carpels. Determinate means of strictly limited growth; sporogenous, bearing the reproductive microspores (male) or megaspores (female). The key portion of this definition, however, is the presence of carpels.

The carpel, characteristic organ of the angiosperms, or "flowering" plants, is an organ bearing and enclosing the ovules; the ovules, in turn, contain the megaspores. Under this definition of a flower, the sporogenous axes of gymnosperms—pine cones, for example—cannot be considered flowers; the absence of true carpels is one of the major characteristics setting off the gymnosperms—conifers, cycads, and the like—from the angiosperms. Strict use of this definition of a flower of course also eliminates those structures,

1

borne by many true angiosperms, which are commonly called "male flowers"—that is, structures containing only the pollen-bearing stamens and without even rudimentary carpels. In practice, the restriction to carpel-bearing structures need not apply here. Studies of flowering in gymnosperms such as pines have been conducted and are, for physiological purposes at any rate, analogous to studies on angiosperms. For these purposes, then, flowering can be taken to mean the production of sporogenous shoots by either angiosperms or gymnosperms; the term flower in its common usage will not be misleading.

The parts of "typical" flowers—such as those found in botany texts—are usually described as follows: the floral axis is more or less shortened as compared with that of a vegetative shoot, and bears successive whorls of parts arranged around it. The structure on which the flower parts are placed is the receptacle, and the stalk bearing the flower is the pedicel. The lowest or outermost parts are the sepals, commonly enclosing the bud; within and above are the petals. Sepals and petals are collectively the perianth. Within this are the stamens, each consisting of a filament bearing a pollen-producing anther. The upper or innermost flower parts are the carpels, which, either singly or united, give rise to one or more ovaries, containing the ovules, and to a pollen-receptive surface, the stigma. Stigma and ovary together, whether derived from one or more carpels, are called the pistil.

Many individual flowers often occur on a single simple or complex axis as in the sunflower (*Helianthus*) or in grasses; such a group of flowers is an inflorescence. Flowers may also be solitary, each borne on a separate pedicel attached to the vegetative axis. Flowers or inflorescences may be terminal (at the ends of shoots) or lateral, or both, and may also be enclosed or accompanied by leafy or scaly bracts.

There are great differences between various plants in the number, arrangement, shape, size, color, degree of fusion, and even presence or absence of the various flower parts. In spite of this, there is a good area of agreement among botanists both on the phylogeny, or evolutionary origin of the flower, and on its ontogeny, or development from the vegetative axis in the individual plant.

The definition of a flower as a particular kind of determinate shoot already implies an interpretation of both phylogeny and ontogeny. The evidence suggests that the various flower parts, from sepals to carpels, are homologous with ordinary foliage leaves. That is, they bear essentially the same anatomical and morphological relation to the axes on which they are borne as do the leaves. This does not necessarily mean that the flower parts have been derived from foliage leaves, even though the flower parts of many plants, particularly those considered more primitive, may show distinctly leaflike characteristics. Probably the most widely accepted view is that both leaves and flower parts were evolutionarily derived from similar structures. These may have been fused branch systems, some of them entirely sterile and represented in our present leaves, some of them sporogenous and represented in modern carpels and anthers, and still others with functions accessory to the sporophylls and represented in modern sepals and petals. While the details of such questions remain speculative for the present since the ancestry of the angiosperms is not really known, the homology between leaves and flower parts is generally accepted and may be of some importance physiologically; it is at least implicitly challenged, however, by some of the work on flower ontogeny to be considered next.

The flower, like the leaves and the shoot itself, is derived from the apical meristem. This is a region of relatively small, undifferentiated, more or less actively dividing cells located at the very apex of the shoot. Meristems in general are the sources of new growth in all higher plants, and this has given rise to the concept that plants, unlike animals, show a "continuing embryogeny." Relatively little is known about the mechanism of the formation of new organs by such embryonic, seemingly slightly organized groups of cells. The central problem of the physiology of flowering might be stated as the question of how various factors affecting flowering, be they environmental or genetic, are translated by the plant into physico-chemical "signals" to the meristem, and how these determine whether the meristem will produce flowers. The major morphological question on which there is disagreement is whether the meristematic activity that produces flower primordia—recognizably distinct structures that will develop into flowers under favorable conditions—is qualitatively different from that which produces leaf initials, which develop into leaves.

According to the majority of recent workers there is no essential difference between the organization of a meristem producing only leaves and one producing flowers. Gross differences of course exist between floral and vegetative apices in a given plant. These differences appear to be correlated with the vegetative and inflorescence structures of the particular plant involved, and no generalizations true for all plants can be made. But the question of essential organization goes beyond this, which is largely a matter of shape and size.

The organization of many vegetative shoot apices can be expressed loosely in terms of the tunica, or outer layers of cells, and the corpus, or inner core of cells, the developmental functions of which may be somewhat different. Most recent investigators have observed that where this organization is present it continues with no sharp change into the floral meristems, which are thus not qualitatively different from the vegetative. See, for examples, Wetmore, Gifford, and Green (1959); Stein and Stein (1960); and Tucker (1960). However, according to a minority of investigators working chiefly in France, floral development is the exclusive function of a "waiting meristem" (*méristème d'attente*) that remains inactive until the onset of flowering, whereas leaf production and purely vegetative growth are carried on by an "initial ring" (*anneau initial*) surrounding it. This work is reviewed by Buvat (1955). In this view, then, reproductive and vegetative development are quite different, originating in different meristem regions, whereas the majority view is that there are not two sorts of development but merely a continuum with extremes.

The view of no essential difference seems to be supported by experimental work, to be described later, showing that certain plants (*Cosmos, Kalanchoë*), given a treatment insufficient to induce flowering but having some effect in that direction, may respond by producing a series of structures intermediate between normal inflorescences and leafy shoots (see Fig. 1-1). Although one can interpret such "vegetative flowering" as the interaction of two fairly distinct meristematic activities, the majority view appears to involve less difficulty.

Descriptive morphology of the meristem has little more to tell the student of flowering physiology, although experimental (operative) morphological studies may well do so in the future. The reader should bear in mind that, in general, experiments on the physiology of flowering have been more concerned with the conditions bringing about the production of flower primordia—with flower initiation, as it is called—than with subsequent flower development, although in practice both are studied.

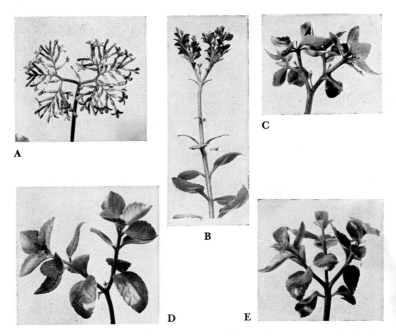

Fig. 1-1. Intermediate conditions between full flowering and vegetative habits in *Kalanchoë blossfeldiana*, from (*A*) normal, fully developed inflorescence through (*B*)-(*D*) increasingly vegetative forms, to (*E*) a fully "vegetative inflorescence" in which there are no flowers at all, but a branching habit still unlike that in the normal vegetative state. The sequence (*A*)-(*E*) reflects decreasing amounts of short-day treatment. (Photographs from Harder [1948], by permission of the company of Biologists, Ltd., and courtesy of Dr. R. Harder, University of Göttingen.)

A concept occasionally found in the experimental literature is that of ripeness-to-flower. In the development of many plants from seed, there may be a stage before which flower initiation cannot occur, at least in response to conditions that would bring it about in older plants. A plant which has passed this stage is said to be ripe-to-flower. This concept will be considered in connection with work requiring it, notably in Chapter Seven, but by itself it explains little about the physiological events taking place and seems not to reflect any basic morphological conditions common to all plants.

For more detailed treatments of the topics discussed here, see Lawrence (1951), Esau (1953), and Foster and Gifford (1959).

NATURAL HISTORY OF FLOWERING

Most of what is known about flowering is based on work done either with plants native to the temperate zone or with cultivated plants. Flowering times and habits particularly have been studied more thoroughly in the higher latitudes than in the tropics. This limitation should be kept in mind in any discussion of flowering habits and physiological mechanisms. The general state of ignorance on flowering in the tropics, and particularly its seasonal aspects, is well summarized by Richards (1957, pp. 199–204).

Plants are often classified as annual, biennial, or perennial. Under these familiar terms a plant either germinates, flowers, and dies within a single season, germinates and develops during one season and flowers and dies in the next, or persists for many years flowering repeatedly. Such classifications are not always physiologically meaningful, although, as will appear later, many biennials can be regarded as annuals in which a low-temperature treatment is required for flower initiation. But many plants commonly called annuals do not die after flowering and fruiting in all climates; they may be tropical perennials able to survive or cultivated as annuals in cooler regions.

There might be more meaning, both ecological and physiological, to a classification into two groups—the first being perennials, defined as above, and the second, a group called monocarpic plants. Under this term can be classified true annuals, such as the edible pea (*Pisum sativum*), biennials, and certain others, all having in common the behavior of flowering only once, with fruiting followed by death. This group then would include plants such as the century plant (*Agave*) that may develop from five to twenty or more years before flowering, and many tropical bamboos, with life spans from two to perhaps over fifty years. Such plants clearly differ somehow from typical perennials that flower and fruit over tens or even hundreds of years without evincing any ill effects.

Many studies of flower initiation and development under natural temperate-zone conditions have been made on individual species. A survey of a large number of species in Britain was reported by Grainger (1939). By determining the times of flower initiation, bud development, and subsequent anthesis (flower opening), Grainger distinguished three classes of temperate-zone plants. Direct-flowering plants are those in which development through anthesis follows on initiation without interruption; this is perhaps the commonest type of flowering behavior, found in both monocarpic and perennial plants. Initiation and anthesis may occur either together with the maximum vegetative growth, as for example in bluebells (*Campanula*) and mint (*Mentha*), or at the period of minimum vegetative growth (winter or early spring) as in *Saxifraga*. A second class, indirect-flowering plants, contains those species in which a distinct period of rest intervenes at some stage between initiation and anthesis. Here again, initiation may coincide with the period of maximum vegetative growth, as in many fruit trees (*Pyrus, Prunus*) and in *Anemone,* or with the period of minimum vegetative growth, as in many bulb flowers (*Tulipa, Narcissus*) that initiate flower primordia in summer after the leaves wither. A third class, cumulative-flowering plants, form primordia over a long period of time, in regular succession, but anthesis of all occurs in a brief period. A number of weed species, notably dandelion (*Taraxacum*), are in this class. Grainger distinguished a fourth class, climax-flowering plants, not found in the temperate zone but including long-lived monocarpic plants such as the bamboos mentioned above.

Most experimental studies of flowering have been conducted on plants of Grainger's first class—direct-flowering plants initiating in the period of maximum vegetative growth. Other types have been studied, however, as will appear in the succeeding chapters. Unfortunately, but for obvious reasons, there has been little if any experimentation on long-lived monocarpic plants.

THE MEASUREMENT OF FLOWERING

The general structure of experiments on flowering is obvious—groups of plants given various treatments are kept under observation until the effects on flowering can be ascertained. The situations may be complicated by the fact that conditions bringing about initiation are not always the same as those favoring bud development, and these in turn may differ from those required for anthesis. As mentioned earlier, experimentalists have been most concerned with initiation; since, however, flower primordia in their earliest stages are detectable only by dissection and microscopy, the data in many studies have been based on the appearance of macroscopic buds or flowers.

Within this general framework, methods of evaluating the results quantitatively are less obvious and vary considerably. The crudest method is simply to record the time required for the first appearance of the designated floral stage in the various treatments. This of course will vary between individuals given the same treatment, so averages are used. Alternative but related data are the percentage of plants in each treatment showing the designated stage at a given time after the start of the experiment. There are also plants, such as soybean (*Glycine*), in which flowering may occur at a number of nodes, and the effectiveness of treatments can be estimated by establishing the average number of nodes with flowers per plant after a given time. Still another related method is that of assigning arbitrary number values to various stages in the development of flower or inflorescence primordia. With a scale so established and an appropriate time for evaluation chosen, the plants in each treatment are dissected or examined and the resulting values averaged. A danger of this method lies in the subjective judgments involved in assessing stages and assigning values to them.

These procedures are all related in that the major independent variable, other than the nature of the treatments given, is time. That is, in a graph of results so obtained, each flowering value, however stated, is a function of time in or after treatment. A drawback of such methods is that if the treatments differ in their effects on overall growth, and the times involved are (as is usual) a week or longer, differences in flowering values may simply reflect differences in growth rate of the entire plant. For example, a 10° C increase in temperature might double the rate of vegetative growth and also that of the appearance of buds. But in such a case the rate of bud appearance *relative* to vegetative growth is unchanged, although time-based data would indicate more rapid flowering.

This sort of danger is widely recognized and it is usually avoided by careful workers. One way of doing this depends on the possibility, which, as will appear, is often present, of using treatments of short duration followed by a return of all the plants to the same conditions where the same rate of growth will be maintained. Or treatments may be found that have demonstrably little direct effect on vegetative growth rate. Another method, often combined with one of these, is to avoid the use of time as a variable.

Instead of time, some index of the rate of vegetative growth can be used as an independent variable. The most common such index is simply the number of new leaves or nodes produced in or after treatment before the designated floral stage appears. The node or leaf index can be substituted for the time scale, and systems can be produced that are analogous to those using time. These matters of scale are not trivial. For instance, an experiment on a time scale might show that treatment A caused 45 percent flowering and treatment B 95 percent flowering after 20 days; the same results on a nodal scale (also after 20 days) might be: A, 100 percent flowering by the third new node; and B, 10 percent flowering by the third new node. Results that "differ" as much as this are not uncommon and require care in interpretation. The reader may find it instructive to invent reasonable data from which such values could arise.

Naturally, the choice of scale depends on the intention of the experimenter. For practical agricultural or horticultural purposes, emphasis is often placed on flowering time. Investigations on more fundamental questions however, such as the existence or non-existence of flower-inducing hormones, are bound to be concerned with flower initiation or development relative to vegetative growth. In the best practice, results are reported in sufficient detail so that the entire developmental situation can be assessed. Very few factors affect flowering exclusively, without modifying vegetative growth. Whether the changes are brought about indirectly, as a result of flowering, or directly, by the factors causing flowering, a plant which is flowering frequently differs from a vegetative one of the same age in height, branching, leaf shape, or pigmentation (to name only a few characteristics), and not simply in the production of flowers. Such changes may provide clues to the mechanisms underlying flower initiation, or they may be effects of flower development itself; in the cases studied so far, it is not clear which.

chapter two ❯ Photoperiodism:
An Outline

For obvious reasons, flowering has been studied largely in plants in which it is controllable by environmental factors that in turn are easily controlled by the plant physiologist. Chief among such factors is the photoperiod, or daily length of illumination. Whether or not it eventually turns out to be as significant for the flowering of most plants as it is for many that have been studied, the following three general statements can be made with certainty.

The phenomenon to be defined as photoperiodism is observed not only among plants but in many animals as well, and is a widespread mechanism in the seasonal regulation of biological processes, particularly reproduction. Although it was first discovered through its connection with flowering, photoperiodism controls other plant processes also, even when it does not affect flowering. Finally, part of the basic mechanism involved in plant photoperiodism occurs in, and can modify the growth of, most higher plant cells and tissues.

DEFINITIONS OF PHOTOPERIODISM

Photoperiodism has been variously defined as a response to the daylength, photoperiod, or daily duration of illumination; as a response to the relative lengths of day and night, or light and darkness; or, in view of later information, as a response to the

10

nightlength or daily duration of darkness. These definitions all convey the general idea, but they may be misleading. A more general definition is that photoperiodism is a response to the duration and timing of the light and dark conditions. Total light quantity, even light intensity above a certain threshold level, is of secondary importance in photoperiodism, although it may be a modifying factor. The relative length, or ratio of the lengths of dark and light exposures, is also secondary. It is the time relations in which light and darkness succeed each other that appear to be crucial.

Under natural conditions of a 24-hour day-night cycle, of course, the duration and timing of light exposure cannot be changed without a complementary change in the dark exposure, but cycle lengths totaling more or less than 24 hours have been used to study photoperiodism experimentally, as have brief light (or dark) interruptions of extended dark (or light) periods. Results from this sort of work have led to the definition given above. In nature, however, the lengths of day and night change seasonally except on the equator, and it is evident that photoperiodism might be expected to have some relation to the seasonal changes in biological events. In fact, it was observations on the relation between seasonal daylengths and flowering that led to the discovery of photoperiodism.

HISTORICAL NOTE

Like many important phenomena, photoperiodism was observed frequently before being finally "discovered." References to early observations by workers such as Tournois, Klebs, and others can be found in Murneek and Whyte (1948), a volume recommended to those interested in the history and early development of flowering physiology. Such observations suggested that flowering in plants such as hops (*Humulus*) or houseleek (*Sempervivum*) could be brought about by artificially shortening or lengthening their daily exposure to light. It remained, however, for Garner and Allard, plant physiologists in the U.S. Department of Agriculture, to show that such effects were not isolated curiosities. It was their early papers (1920, 1923) that attracted other workers to the field and in which the term "photoperiodism" first appeared, although the definition favored above is not their original one. These papers are among the classics of plant physiology; not only do they outline many of the major problems still facing students of photoperiodism, but they are also models of the critical, at first almost reluctant, demonstration of what then seemed a revolutionary concept. Although there is no intention here to maintain a historical approach, a brief outline of two practical problems faced and explained by Garner and Allard will serve as a concrete introduction to photoperiodism.

GIANT TOBACCO AND SEPTEMBER SOYBEANS

The preceding heading might well have been used by Garner and Allard to summarize the problems that led to their discovery. The tobacco, *Nicotiana tabacum*, was a mutant named Maryland Mammoth since it grew over 10 feet high in an experimental plot at Beltsville, Maryland. It nevertheless remained vegetative, thus frustrating its growers who wanted to use it in breeding experiments. Propagated by cuttings and grown in the greenhouse in the winter, however, the mammoth flowered and set seed when less than five feet high. Equally puzzling was the behavior of the Biloxi variety of soybean, *Glycine* (or *Soja*) *max*. When successive sowings were made at two-week intervals from early May through July, all of them showed their first flowers in September, so that the earliest planted had taken some 120 days to flower and the latest about 60. It was as if all were waiting for some signal at which to start flowering, irrespective of their age from germination—an improbable notion that turned out to be correct.

After eliminating other factors such as temperature variations, nutrition, and light intensity, Garner and Allard concluded that the length of day was controlling flowering in both situations. Both Biloxi soybean and Maryland Mammoth tobacco are short-day plants, a term introduced by Garner and Allard. Neither will flower unless the daylength is shorter than a certain critical number of hours (which happens to be different for the two plants). On sufficiently short days, flowering takes place. Thus Maryland Mammoth flowered in the greenhouse in winter under the naturally short days of that season, but merely vegetated and grew large in the field in summer and fall. Biloxi soybeans, no matter when they were planted, would not flower until the sufficiently short days of late summer. Garner and Allard were able to show all this experimentally both by artificially shortening the summer days (placing the plants in light-tight sheds or cabinets at various times) or artificially lengthening winter or fall days even with dim incandescent lights. They also examined the effects of various daylengths on other plants and discovered various kinds of flowering responses, as well as many other effects. Work on photoperiodism soon became world-wide and has remained so, with major contributions coming from Britain, France, Germany, Italy, Japan, the Netherlands, Russia, the United States, and elsewhere.

KINDS OF PHOTOPERIODIC FLOWERING RESPONSES

The flowering responses of various plants to different daylengths in a normal 24-hour cycle can be roughly grouped into the following classes, of which the first two are those commonly studied.

1. _Short-Day Plants:_ The abbreviation SDP will be adopted for these hereafter. Flower initiation in SDP is promoted by daylengths shorter than a particular value, the so-called critical daylength, which differs widely from species to species. It is probably actually the nightlength that is the most critical factor in such plants; hence, they have been described as "long-night plants." Much more work has been done with SDP than with the other classes. Examples are Maryland Mammoth tobacco and Biloxi soybeans, discussed above, also the common cocklebur, _Xanthium,_ and the succulent _Kalanchoë blossfeldiana._ See the illustration facing page 1 and Fig. 2-1 for two examples of SDP.

2. _Long-Day Plants:_ The abbreviation LDP will be used for these. Flower initiation is promoted by daylengths longer than a particular value, the critical daylength, which differs from species to species. Again, such plants have also been described as "short-night plants." Examples are the Black Henbane, _Hyoscyamus niger,_ and some varieties of barley, _Hordeum vulgare._

3 and 4. _Short-Long-_ and _Long-Short-Day Plants:_ Flower

initiation in a relatively few plants appears to be promoted by successive exposures to the kinds of conditions promoting it in classes 1 and 2, in an order depending upon the particular species. Each requirement in a given species may have its own critical daylength. Such plants have been little studied but may be valuable

Fig. 2-1. Short-day response in morning glory (*Ipomoea hederacea* var. Scarlett O'Hara). Plants are about 8 weeks old, all grown with 8 hours of sunlight per day. In addition, the plant to the right received a further 8 hours per day of dim (40 foot candles) incandescent light for a total photoperiod of 16 hours. (Photograph from Hendricks [1956], *American Scientist*, **44**: 229–247, by permission of the board of editors of the *American Scientist* and courtesy of Drs. H. A. Borthwick and S. B. Hendricks, U. S. Department of Agriculture.)

in analyzing the photoperiodic mechanism. Some varieties of wheat, *Triticum vulgare,* and rye, *Secale cereale,* may be short-long-day plants; some *Bryophyllum* species and the night-blooming jasmine, *Cestrum nocturnum,* are long-short-day plants.

5. *Day-Neutral or Daylength-Indifferent Plants:* These simply flower after reaching a certain age or size and apparently irrespective of daylength. Other processes, however, may be photo-

periodically controlled. Flowering in such plants, which may constitute the majority, has been relatively little studied. Common examples are tomato, *Lycopersicon esculentum,* and many varieties of peas, *Pisum sativum.*

Note that in this classification the distinction between SDP and LDP is based not on the absolute values of the critical daylengths (which may range from four to over 18 hours for LDP, for example); the distinction is whether flowering is promoted by photoperiods shorter or longer than the critical. The critical daylength for *Xanthium,* for example, is about 15½ hours, and that for *Hyoscyamus* about 11 hours. Yet the former is properly classified as an SDP since it flowers on photoperiods shorter than its critical value, whereas the latter is an LDP, requiring photoperiods longer than its critical. It is necessary to belabor this distinction since it is possible to find textbooks that should know better implying that LDP flower with more hours of light per day than SDP. Such statements miss the point. Both *Xanthium* and *Hyoscyamus* flower with 14 hours of light per day. The daylength in which a plant flowers is no indication of its response class in the absence of further information.

In addition to the classes of response described, the following considerations should be recognized before proceeding further. There are plants in which the appropriate photoperiodic treatment is an absolute requirement for flowering under all naturally occurring conditions. Neither *Xanthium* nor *Hyoscyamus,* for example, ever flowers unless exposed to the proper photoperiodic conditions. Such plants are referred to as having a qualitative photoperiodic response, or requirement. In other plants, differing photoperiodic conditions merely hasten or delay but do not absolutely determine flower initiation. Such plants have a quantitative response to photoperiod. There are also plants in which qualitative or quantitative photoperiodic responses are observed only under particular conditions of temperature or some other environmental factors; these would be conditional photoperiodic responses. Still other plants may require one photoperiodic condition for flower initiation but a markedly different one for flower development. Finally, there are many species in which the photoperiodic response may change with age; such changes are usually in the direction of day-neutrality from an initial qualitative or quantitative long- or short-day response.

A particularly clear example of the last sort of behavior is shown by a variety of sunflower, *Helianthus annuus,* recently studied by Dyer *et al.* (1959). Seedlings raised under 12-hour daylengths all showed inflorescences after 40 days, while seedlings raised under 16-hour daylengths showed no detectable flower primordia at the time. Over 90 percent flowering occurred on both 12- and 16-hour photoperiods in experiments carried to 130 days, however, and even 20-hour photoperiods gave over 70 percent flowering. In other words, young plants had a qualitative short-day response with a critical daylength between 12 and 16 hours, but older plants were either day-neutral or showed a weak quantitative short-day response.

While this brief list by no means exhausts the ways in which photoperiodic responses may differ within the overall classification, and examples will appear frequently in what follows, there do appear to be limits on such variation. Although varieties of the same species often differ in critical daylength and frequently show a range from day-neutrality to a qualitative long- or short-day requirement, the writer knows of no species with both LDP and SDP varieties; it is even relatively unusual to find both types within a single genus. The range of variation that can be caused by age or environmental conditions is also apparently limited in the same way as that within a species; that is, no experimental treatment yet found will convert an LDP to an SDP, or vice versa. Such an effect would obviously be very valuable for studies of the mechanism involved. Aside from these generalizations, however, the responses of species and varieties within a given class are extremely various, and there is no evident correlation between photoperiodic response classes and any taxonomic or ecological category. Thus, although much of this discussion will proceed by considering some of the results from a few well-studied plants, let the reader beware: the country is large, and the map, so far, is small. For many variations and modifications in photoperiodic response that have not been studied systematically, see Chouard (1957).

THE ROLE OF LEAVES IN PHOTOPERIODISM. PHOTOPERIODIC INDUCTION

Neither of these topics will be considered in detail until Chapter Five where the discussion is on the nature of the flowering stimulus, since both are more germane to that question than to photoperiodism proper. Brief summaries are given here simply to render the rest of this chapter intelligible.

In almost every plant studied, it is the leaf blades that perceive the photoperiodic treatment. This has been shown in several ways. Photoperiodic treatments given to all, or in some cases one or a few, leaf blades on a plant will have the same effects as though the entire plant had been treated. Defoliated plants, with rare exceptions, are photoperiodically unresponsive. Photoperiodic treatment of the apices or other meristematic areas is usually ineffective, although the meristems are the actual sites of the change from vegetative to reproductive growth. One can conclude that the primary photoperiodic effect occurs in the leaves and that the leaves somehow communicate its results to the meristems.

Certain plants require more or less constant exposure to appropriate photoperiodic cycles, at least until flower primordia can be easily detected, in order to flower successfully. In many others, however, exposure to only a few such cycles will cause flowering even when the plants are returned to unfavorable photoperiodic conditions. Such plants are said to be induced by the photoperiodic treatment; photoperiodic induction is an aftereffect of favorable photoperiods which will result in flowering or at least considerable primordium development, even on unfavorable photoperiods. An induced plant indicates clearly by this behavior that some change has taken place and persists, but no anatomical or morphological changes can usually be detected after the few inductive cycles required in such plants. Naturally, not only is induction of great theoretical interest but it is also experimentally useful. One of the major reasons for the widespread use of *Xanthium* in photoperiodic studies is that, under favorable conditions, a single short-day cycle (even given to a single leaf) will lead to flowering in plants kept the rest of the time on noninductive long days. This sensitivity to a single cycle is unusual, but is not unique to *Xanthium;* it has been reported also in the Japanese morning glory, *Pharbitis* (or *Ipomoea*) *nil* (Imamura and Takimoto, 1955a), a duckweed, *Lemna perpusilla* (Hillman, 1959a), and pigweeds, *Chenopodium* (Cumming, 1959), all SDP. Many other SDP also can be induced by 2 to 10 days of the appropriate photoperiodic treatment. Induction by a very few cycles is perhaps less common among LDP, although at least dill, *Anethum graveolens* (A. W. Naylor, 1941), and mature plants of the grass *Lolium temulentum* (Evans, 1960) are both inducible by one long-day cycle.

THE CENTRAL ROLE OF THE DARK PERIOD

While the terms "short-day" and "long-day" plant have been maintained by constant usage, probably the most important single difference between these two response classes is in their reactions to the nightlength, or dark period. In general, flowering in SDP is promoted by certain reactions taking place during the dark periods, and the "critical daylength" actually represents the maximum daylength that will allow a dark period of sufficient length in a normal 24-hour cycle. In LDP, on the other hand, dark periods have an inhibitory effect on flower initiation, and the critical daylength is thus the minimum which in a 24-hour cycle will keep the dark period short enough to allow flowering. These generalizations are supported by the fact that LDP usually flower best on continuous light, so that apparently the entire role of the dark period is inhibitory (A. W. Naylor, 1941; see Lang, 1952). Several SDP, on the contrary, flower in continuous darkness if they are given sucrose (see Doorenbos and Wellensiek, 1959; Hillman, 1959a), suggesting that light is unnecessary if its photosynthetic function is replaced by another source of carbohydrate. However, at least one LDP, spinach, *Spinacia oleracea,* also flowers in total darkness when supplied with sucrose (Gentscheff and Gustaffson, 1940) so that reliance on this sort of evidence alone is undesirable.

Hamner and Bonner (1938) were able to show that in *Xanthium* the critical time for an appropriate photoperiodic treatment lay in the dark period length. When 24-hour cycles of light and darkness were used, these plants flowered with dark periods of 8½ hours or longer. Thus the critical daylength was 15½ hours. No flowering occurred on schedules of 16 hours light-

8 hours darkness. To determine whether it was actually the day-length or nightlength that was critical in this schedule, Hamner and Bonner performed several kinds of experiments.

Using artificial light when necessary, they exposed some plants to schedules of 4 hours light-8 hours darkness. None of these flowered, although each light period was far shorter than the critical daylength of 15½ hours. On the other hand, all plants flowered rapidly under cycles of 16 hours light-32 hours darkness, even though each light period was longer than the critical daylength. Two conclusions come from such data. First, it seems to be the length of the dark period, not that of the light period, that is important for *Xanthium*. Second, the relative length of day and night is clearly not the critical factor since the ratio of light to darkness was the same in both schedules used.

Perhaps the best evidence concerning the role of the dark period in both LDP and SDP can be obtained by interrupting these dark periods with brief light exposures. Hamner and Bonner, for example, showed that the inductive effects of 9-hour dark periods could be completely annulled by interrupting each one in the middle with a minute of relatively dim (150 foot candles) incandescent light. This "light-break" effect is widespread among both response classes, and the general situation can be summarized as follows (see, for example, Borthwick, Hendricks, and Parker, 1956).

In order to be photoperiodically effective in either SDP or LDP, a dark period of sufficient length has to be uninterrupted. Total light energies (100–1000 kiloergs/cm²) that are very low compared to those of daylight, even given in a few minutes, are sufficient to constitute an effective interruption. In SDP such as *Xanthium* or Biloxi soybeans, light-breaks in otherwise inductive dark periods will completely inhibit flowering. In LDP such as *Hyoscyamus* or the Wintex variety of barley, *Hordeum vulgare*, light-breaks in otherwise noninductive periods (that is, in schedules with daylengths less than the critical) bring about flowering as though the plants had been on an adequate long-day schedule. As will become evident later on, light-break experiments have proved very useful for further studies on the mechanism of photoperiodism. At this juncture, however, they are simply presented as evidence for the role of the dark periods as the single most important controlling factor in photoperiodism. Similarly, brief "dark-breaks" during main light periods have essentially no effect on the process.

The evidence reviewed above should make clear the reason for emphasizing duration and timing of light (and darkness) rather than total energy in the definition of photoperiodism. It has also resulted in the term "critical nightlength" replacing "critical daylength" in some reviews and articles on the subject, in order to stress the relative importance of light and dark periods. However, as will be shown, light also plays a role, although perhaps less important, in the normal time requirements of photoperiodism, so that the second terminology is only slightly more accurate than the first. Either will be used, as occasion demands.

Ancillary evidence for the more crucial role of the dark periods has also been derived from experiments in which temperature is varied, some of which will be considered elsewhere.

REQUIREMENTS FOR HIGH-INTENSITY LIGHT
(for photisynthesis)

The effects of brief or prolonged exposures to low-intensity light, nullifying dark periods, will be considered in detail in the next chapter. Meanwhile, after setting up generalizations that darkness plays the major role in photoperiodism and that the total light energy during a treatment or cycle is relatively unimportant, it is now necessary to consider what role, if any, is played by the high-intensity light periods which, at least in nature, normally alternate with dark periods.

1. *Short-Day Plants:* Early work with SDP soon showed that in spite of the critical role of the dark periods, the main light periods also had to include at least a certain amount of high-intensity light for optimum flowering to occur in many plants. An elegant demonstration of this was given by Hamner (1940), using *Xanthium*.

It was obviously not reasonable to study the effect of a dark period preceded by a dark period, since the two together simply add up to a longer one. Hamner made use of the light-break technique, however, in the following manner. *Xanthium* plants can be kept vegetative on cycles of 3 minutes light-3 hours darkness. After a few such cycles, a single dark period of 12 hours, which would normally cause flowering if the plants were subsequently placed on long-day conditions, was entirely ineffective. Before such a dark period could be effective, the plants had to be exposed to at least a few hours of high-intensity light; within limits, the effectiveness of the dark period was then directly related to the light energy given before it. This "high-intensity light reaction" clearly differs from the low-intensity reaction sufficient to interrupt a dark period, since it requires light energies some 10,000 times higher for maximum effect. It has since been shown that CO_2 must be present for the high-intensity light to have its effect; in addition, feeding the leaves with carbohydrates or organic acids can at least partially replace the high-intensity light requirement (see Liverman, 1955). Such results suggest that this requirement is largely a requirement for products of photosynthesis.

Another high-intensity light requirement has also been reported in *Xanthium*. To be maximally effective, an inductive dark period must be followed as well as preceded by a period of high-intensity light. Lockhart and Hamner (1954), for example, found that if only a brief light flash was given to end the inductive dark period and this was then followed by another dark period before the plants were replaced in long-day conditions, flowering was completely or partially inhibited. A period of high-intensity light given before the second (inhibitory) dark period rendered it ineffective, but low-intensity light did not. Both auxin (see Chapter Six) and high temperature increased the effect of the second dark period. Subsequently, Carr (1957) found that sucrose given to the leaf during the second dark period almost nullified the inhibition, allowing flowering to take place. He thus suggested that the "second high-intensity light requirement," like the first, is a requirement for photosynthetic products.

While experiments of this sort show that high-intensity light periods can have profound modifying effects on photoperiodic induction, these are probably due to effects of photosynthate as an energy source and on the translocation of the flowering stimulus (see Chapter Five) rather than on photoperiodism proper. Even *Xanthium*, on which the most detailed work of this kind has been done, can eventually initiate flowers in total darkness (Hamner, 1940). Thus the primary role of the dark period in photoperiodism is not contradicted by these data.

The interpretation of high-intensity light requirements in SDP as basically photosynthetic is not entirely secure. *Kalanchoë blossfeldiana* is an SDP incapable of flowering in continuous darkness. It will, however, initiate flowers if it receives one one-second flash of light in every 24 hours (see Harder, 1948; Schwabe, 1959). Although CO_2 is indeed required during the light flash, it is not likely that a great deal of photosynthesis takes place during that time, so that a more specific requirement is at least suggested.

Even the generalization that the photoperiodic responses of SDP are generally promoted by at least some exposure to high-intensity light does not hold for the widely studied *Perilla*. Using *Perilla crispa,* de Zeeuw (1953) found that the critical daylength becomes longer (dark requirement becomes shorter) as the main light period intensity is lowered; with sufficiently low light intensities, flower initiation occurs under continuous light. A set of experiments on the complex interactions of bright and dim light periods on *Kalanchoë* has been published by Krumwiede (1960), who also provides a thorough bibliography on the question. It seems clear that probably more factors than photosynthesis are involved in the effects of bright light.

2. *Long-day Plants:* Since, in general, the longer the light period the better for flowering in LDP, analyses of the kind described above have attracted little interest. A number of LDP are nevertheless known to flower more rapidly in either continuous light or long photoperiods if at least part of each light exposure is at high intensity (see Bonner and Liverman, 1953). Much of the work on the main light periods of LDP, like some of that on SDP, has been on the effects of various light colors, and will be considered in the next chapter.

MUTUAL INTERACTIONS OF LIGHT AND DARK PERIOD LENGTHS

Extremely complex interactions between light and dark period lengths have been observed in both LDP and SDP, to the extent that the critical values of either light or dark periods are markedly affected by the lengths of the complementary periods.

Claes and Lang (1947) studied the effects of various light and dark schedules on the rapidity with which the LDP *Hyoscyamus niger* would initiate flowers. As long as the light-dark cycles totaled 24 hours, flowering occurred with at least 11 hours of light per cycle, and was most rapid with 15–16 hours. When cycles totaling 48 hours were used, however, flowering occurred with as few as 9 hours light per cycle, and reached its maximum rapidity with 13 hours per cycle. Thus longer total cycle lengths actually reduced the "critical daylength" by at least two hours, in spite of the fact that the shorter daylength was active with a much longer dark period.

Differing but equally complex results were obtained by Takimoto (1955) in experiments in which he exposed the LDP *Silene armeria* to 10-day treatments of cycles composed of various durations of light and darkness. Flower initiation was most rapid in continuous light. In cycles with light periods of 12 hours or shorter, initiation occurred only when the associated dark periods were shorter than 13 hours; in cycles with light periods of 14 or 16 hours, however, even dark periods of 24 or 32 hours duration failed to prevent initiation. Some of the interactions between light and dark periods in the SDP Biloxi soybeans were studied by Blaney and Hamner (1957). Only a few of the results will be mentioned here, but this paper provides one of the best examples of the complexity of such interactions and resultant difficulty of reaching any general conclusions on the problem at present. The Biloxi soybean, like most SDP, requires several cycles of appropriate photoperiodic treatment to initiate flowers. When plants were given 7 cycles of 8 hours fluorescent light and 16 hours darkness, then placed on long-day greenhouse conditions, high flowering values were obtained. Hence 8-hour light periods and 16-hour dark periods together constitute an inductive cycle. However, when each portion of such an inductive cycle was examined separately, the following results were obtained. Seven cycles of 8 hours light alternating with 24-hour or 26-hour dark periods resulted in no induction at all. Seven cycles of 16-hour dark periods alternating with light periods either 4 hours or shorter, or longer than 12 hours, also resulted in no induction. For further results and tentative conclusions the original paper should be consulted. The concept of a minimum critical dark period requirement was still supported since induction was never brought about by any cycle with less than a 10-hour dark period, no matter what the associated light period; however, it also did not occur on cycles containing 16-hour light periods, no matter what the dark period.

The generalization that crucial events in photoperiodism take place during the dark period is evidently not annulled by results such as those presented in this section. The precise values of "critical nightlengths," however, are markedly dependent upon the lengths of the associated light periods, and in a manner which conforms to no simple pattern.

INTERACTION OF DIFFERENT PHOTOPERIODIC CYCLES: FRACTIONAL INDUCTION IN LDP AND LONG-DAY INHIBITION IN SDP

In all the experiments so far considered, not more than one particular kind of light-dark cycle was used for each experimental treatment, although such cycles might be repeated several times. It is desirable to examine some results of using more than one kind of cycle in a given treatment. Most such experiments have been concerned with the effects of intercalating noninductive between inductive cycles, and have naturally been conducted largely with plants requiring more than one cycle for induction. The responses of LDP and SDP to such treatments differ fairly consistently from each other, but show considerable regularity within each class.

Most LDP studied are susceptible to "fractional induction." This is best illustrated by an example reported by Snyder (1948). Plants of the plantain *Plantago lanceolata* showed 100 percent inflorescences after exposure to 25 long-day cycles (18 hours light-6 hours darkness). Exposure to only 10 such cycles resulted in no flowering when followed by exposure to short-day cycles (8 hours light-16 hours darkness). However, if 10 long-day cycles were given and followed by 20 short-day cycles, only 15 more long-day cycles were required for 100 percent inflorescence formation. Thus the effect of the first 10 inductive cycles, though insufficient to cause flowering by itself, persisted throughout the short-day treatment so that only 15 more long-day cycles gave the effective total of 25. This remarkably accurate "memory" is apparently not unusual in fractional induction. It implies that, in such LDP at least, non-inductive cycles play a merely passive role and do not oppose the effects of inductive cycles.

In several SDP, on the other hand, noninductive cycles have a clearly inhibiting action on induction. Schwabe (1959) has shown that for *Perilla ocymoides, Chenopodium amaranticolor,* and Biloxi soybean, noninductive cycles intercalated between inductive cycles positively inhibit the effects of the latter. Each long-day cycle, in fact, appears capable of counteracting the effect of two short-day cycles. A long-day cycle probably acts by annulling the effectiveness of the short days immediately following it, rather than by destroying the effect of the short days preceding it. Such a conclusion agrees with the results of Harder and Bünsow (1954) who had found that the number of flowers formed by *Kalanchoë blossfeldiana* after a given number of short-day cycles was inversely related to the daylength used in the noninductive cycles on which the plants were kept previous to short-day treatment. However, Carr (1955) obtained fractional induction in a number of SDP, including some of the same plants used by Schwabe, above. Carr also cites other results that oppose the generalization that only LDP exhibit the phenomenon, holding instead that it shows no particular correlation with response type but rather is an individual species characteristic.

Possibly the ability of *Xanthium* and a few other SDP to flower in response to one short-day cycle is due to the lack, or weaker operation, of inhibitory long-day effects. Even in *Xanthium,* of course, flowering intensity increases proportionately to the number of short-day cycles over a considerable range (see Chapter Five) so that the phenomenon may be quite general.

PHOTOPERIODISM AND TEMPERATURE

Temperature enters into the physiology of flowering in numerous ways, many of which will be considered later. A few interactions of temperature with photoperiodism will be mentioned now, but with the cautionary note that the results of such studies tend to defy generalization more completely than any other aspect of the field. For a major treatment of the effects of temperature on plant growth, see Went (1957).

Temperatures differing slightly from one another may strongly modify the effects of daylength on flower initiation. For example, Roberts and Struckmeyer (1938) found that both Maryland Mammoth tobacco and Jimson weed, *Datura stramonium,* were SDP only at 24° C or higher, but tended toward day-neutrality at about 13° C. Strawberry, *Fragaria virginiana* x *chiloensis,* shows a virtually identical response (Went, 1957, Chap. 11). The requirement of at least a flash of bright light for induction of *Kalanchoë,* mentioned previously, has been confirmed by Oltmanns (1960) at 20° or 25°, but apparently is no longer present at 15° C, since *Kalanchoë* will initiate flowers in total darkness at that temperature.

The critical daylength for certain LDP is reduced at low temperatures. *Hyoscyamus niger* grown at 28.5° C requires at least 11½ hours of light per day to flower, whereas at 15.5° the critical daylength is reduced to 8½ hours (see Melchers and Lang, 1948). However, the LDP *Rudbeckia bicolor* will flower at relatively high temperatures (about 32° C) under photoperiods too short to permit flowering under cool conditions; *Rudbeckia speciosa,* a similar species, remains a true LDP under both conditions (Murneek, 1940).

Most effects of this kind have been ascribed primarily to dark period rather than light period temperatures (see Lang, 1952), but unusual temperatures can modify both light and dark period processes. Two of the early papers on *Xanthium* illustrate this point.

Long (1939) found that *Xanthium* required at least six cycles of 9 hours light-15 hours darkness for induction if the dark period temperature was 5° C, even though the light periods were given at 21° C. Further experiments showed that when plants were grown at 21° light temperature and 5° dark temperature, the critical nightlength was increased to about 11 hours compared with 8⅓ hours for plants held constantly at 21°. Long concluded that "variations in temperature greatly affect the length of the critical dark period," although his work has been cited, in a context to be discussed later, as showing a "relatively temperature-independent time measurement of nightlength" (Pittendrigh and Bruce, 1959).

The light period processes in *Xanthium* also are temperature-sensitive, at least when they are made relatively limiting (Mann, 1940). At least four hours of bright light (over 2000 foot candles) are required for the optimum action of a subsequent dark period if the light is given at 10° C, but only about one half hour of light is required at 30° for the same effect.

The sensitivity of light or dark periods to temperature changes has been studied extensively in connection with the possible rhythmic components of photoperiodism (see Chapter Three). The paper by Blaney and Hamner, previously cited, also contains data on the interactions of temperature with the various light-dark cycles used. A simpler example of such work is a paper by Schwemmle (1957) reporting the effects on the SDP *Kalanchoë blossfeldiana* of brief exposures to 30° C during various portions of 12-hour dark periods alternated with 12-hour light periods (inductive for *Kalanchoë*), the temperature otherwise being 20°. Such exposures promoted flowering significantly when given for the first three hours of each dark period, but inhibited it completely when given for the last three hours. Full 12-hour exposures to 30° during the night also inhibited completely.

One of the most striking temperature effects reported recently deals again with *Xanthium,* which will apparently flower on a 16 hours light-8 hours darkness schedule, completely noninductive at 23° C, if the first 8 hours of each light period are given at 4°. Low temperatures during the second half of each light period, or during the dark period itself, do not cause flowering, nor does flowering occur on continuous light with any alternation of temperatures used (Nitsch and Went, 1959); see Fig. 2-2. The SDP *Pharbitis* can be brought to flower even under continuous light by low-temperature treatments (Ogawa, 1960).

On the basis of some experiments with *Hyoscyamus* and the SDP *Chenopodium,* as well as other results in the literature, Schwemmle (1960) has suggested in a brief paper that, in a physiological sense, high temperatures may be equivalent to light and low temperatures to darkness in their effects on photoperiodism. Whether this generalization will withstand critical examination remains to be seen. So far, all that can be said with certainty is that high or low temperatures can modify both dark and light processes in photoperiodism in a manner varying widely with the temperatures, species, specific cycle, and portion of light or dark period chosen.

PHOTOPERIODISM AND VEGETATIVE GROWTH

Structures and processes of all kinds can be affected by photoperiodism, and such results are widespread in the literature,

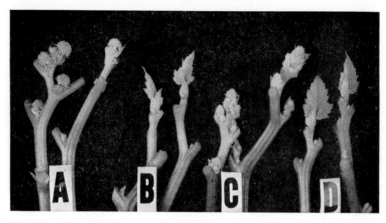

Fig. 2-2. Photoperiodic control of flowering in cocklebur (*Xanthium pennsylvanicum*) as modified by low temperature. Growing points of plants of the same age—with all except terminal leaves removed to show development—photographed after 13 days of the following treatments: (*A*) 8-hour days at 23° C (flowering); (*B*) 16-hour days at 23° C (vegetative); (*C*) 16-hour days as in (*B*) but with 4° during first 8 hours of each light period; (*D*) 24-hour (continuous) days at 23° except 4° during 8 hours of each day. (Photographs from Nitsch and Went [1959], by permission of the American Association for the Advancement of Science and courtesy of Dr. J. P. Nitsch, *Le Phytotron*, Gif-sur-Yvette, France.)

starting with Garner and Allard. Some of the characteristics frequently under photoperiodic control even when flowering is not are stem elongation, leaf shape and size, branching, pigmentation, tuberization, and pubescence (see, for example, Naylor, 1953). Effects on these have been studied far less than the flowering responses, but the data at hand suggest that they are less likely to be inductive. That is, when the photoperiodic conditions are changed, the new vegetative growth quickly reflects the new conditions. This may even be true when the vegetative change would normally be associated with a truly inductive effect on flowering. In Murneek's work on *Rudbeckia bicolor,* for example, continuous treatment with long days (longer than 12 hours) caused both flowering and stem elongation. Exposure to only 25 long days still brought about flowering, both normal and abnormal, but the plants remained in a semirosette stage.

Many papers on responses of all types make it difficult to decide whether they are truly photoperiodic or not. Paradoxically, this is more often true in very recent research, since air conditioning now makes it possible to grow plants entirely under high intensities of artificial light. This frequently results in comparisons between plants grown, for example, in 8 and 16 hours of light per day, comparisons with the implicit or explicit assumption that the operative difference between treatments is in light duration, even though the total light energies also differ proportionately (see, for example, Galston and Kaur, 1961; also portions of Went, 1957). It would help clarify the literature if the term photoperiodic were properly restricted to effects that have been concurrently or previously shown to be controlled by light and dark duration and timing, as indicated by light-breaks or low-intensity supplementary illumination. Any other use of the term only results in confounding photoperiodism with the effects of greatly increased or decreased photosynthesis, or other light actions.

LITERATURE

The literature on photoperiodism is vast. Some of the most useful reviews are by Lang (1952), Naylor (1953), Bonner and Liverman (1953), Borthwick, Hendricks, and Parker (1956), and Doorenbos and Wellensiek (1959). A volume edited by the late R. B. Withrow (1959) contains many valuable reviews and original reports on photoperiodism and related phenomena in both plants and animals.

chapter three > Photoperiodism:

Attempts at Analysis

Faced with the various phenomena of the previous chapter, many investigators of photoperiodism have naturally tried to discover characteristics common to the various response classes, and particularly to look for indications of whatever cellular and biochemical mechanisms might be involved. Two major lines of such research, by no means completely separate, are the subject of this chapter.

A. PHOTOPERIODISM AND LIGHT QUALITY

So far, photoperiodism has been considered simply in terms of white light versus darkness, but experiments with light quality— different colors or wavelengths of light—have proved very valuable. They have opened up photoperiodism itself to further manipulation and linked it to a biochemical system, still incompletely known, that is probably universal among plants except perhaps for the bacteria and fungi. The main point of departure for this work was the effectiveness of relatively brief, low-energy "light-breaks" in opposing the flower-promoting or flower-inhibiting (for LDP) effects of appropriate dark periods.

ACTION SPECTRA FOR LIGHT-BREAKS

In order to act on any process, light must first be absorbed. Compounds, called pigments, that absorb visible light are generally complex organic compounds, although many inorganic salts are highly colored. The absorption spectrum of a given pigment, by which is meant a curve indicating the relative degree to which it absorbs various wavelengths of light, is characteristic of that compound alone, or at least of a small class of similar substances. Thus

Fig. 3-1. Method of holding single leaves (these are soybean leaflets) in the image plane of a spectrograph for subsequent irradiation with various wavelengths of light. (Photograph from Hendricks and Borthwick, *Proc. First Int. Photobiol. Cong.* [1954], courtesy of Dr. H. A. Borthwick, U. S. Department of Agriculture.)

the action spectrum for any process affected by light—a curve indicating the relative effectiveness of different wavelengths on the process—may provide information as to the nature of the compound or compounds by which the light is absorbed. For example, part of the evidence for the role of chlorophyll in photosynthesis is the observation that the light most active in that process—blue, wavelengths 4000–4500 Å (Ångstrom units), and red, 6200–6800 Å—is also the light most strongly absorbed by chlorophyll solutions. That is, the action spectrum for photosynthesis resembles the absorption spectrum of chlorophyll solutions.

In principle, this seems simple enough; in fact, the accurate determination and evaluation of absorption and action spectra is a complex, still-developing branch of physics and chemistry, as well as biology; for some references, see articles in Hollaender (1956) and Withrow (1959). For present purposes, however, it should be evident that the action spectra for light-break effects in various plants might indicate whether or not these effects are mediated by the same pigment and what that pigment might be.

Much of the work on this question has been done by Garner and Allard's successors, a group at the U.S. Department of Agriculture, Beltsville, Maryland, and many reviews by the original workers are in the literature (see, for example, Borthwick, Hendricks, and Parker, 1956; Borthwick, 1959; Hendricks, 1958, 1959). Their procedures are basically simple, though not technically easy. Stating the situation more quantitatively than before, an action spectrum can be represented either as a graph of varying responses brought about by equal energies of light of given wavelengths, or as a graph of the energy which must be given at each wavelength to cause a particular degree of response. Thus it is necessary to measure the effect of each wavelength chosen at several energy levels, and on a considerable number of plants; this requires light of considerable intensities but in relatively pure wavelength bands spread out over considerable areas. For this purpose, the Beltsville group built a large spectrograph, in which high-intensity white light could be passed through a prism and projected as a spectrum. They then took advantage of the fact that in the plants chosen photoperiodic treatments need only be given to a single leaf if the other leaves were removed. The single leaf could be placed so as to receive light of a particular color and energy at the optimal time for dark period interruptions; after many such experiments, the relative effectiveness of the various colors can be calculated. (See Figs. 3-1 and 3-2.)

From 1946 on, action spectra for light-break responses were obtained in both SDP and LDP, including *Xanthium,* Biloxi soybean, *Hyoscyamus,* and Wintex barley. All these spectra seem substantially alike; the most effective wavelengths are in the orange-red range, 6000–6800, with a maximum at 6400–6600 and a steep drop beyond 6800 Å. Blue light is much less effective and green is almost completely ineffective. Such results indicated that

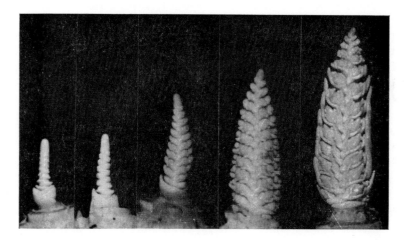

Fig. 3-2. Effects of various amounts of light given as dark-period interruptions on inflorescence primordium development in the LDP barley (*Hordeum vulgare* var. Wintex). Three-week-old plants were grown for 9 days with 12½-hour dark periods interrupted in the middle with various energies of light, then allowed to grow for 19 days with uninterrupted dark periods. These dissections show the apices greatly magnified; that at the far right was about 3 mm high. Relative energies used for the night interruptions ranged from none (extreme left) through 25 (middle) to 400 (extreme right) foot-candle minutes of white light. The study of similarly graded responses to various energies at various wavelengths indicated the effectiveness of the wavelengths tested. (Photograph from Borthwick, Hendricks, and Parker [1948], *Bot. Gaz.*, **110:** 103–118, courtesy of Dr. H. A. Borthwick, U. S. Department of Agriculture.)

light-breaks inhibiting the flowering of SDP were probably absorbed by the same pigment as those promoting flowering in LDP. The nature of the pigment remained a subject of speculation since no known pigment in higher plants had an absorption spectrum with a peak only in the red region. Further information came from outside photoperiodism proper, and it is therefore necessary to digress.

THE RED, FAR-RED REVERSIBLE SYSTEM

It had been known for a long time, in a general way, that the germination of many seeds was affected by light. Flint and Mc-Alister (1935, 1937) had found that the germination of lettuce, *Lactuca sativa,* was promoted by red light. If seeds previously exposed to enough red to cause subsequent germination were exposed to either blue or near-infrared (7000–8000 Å) light, germination was inhibited. This work was taken up again by the Beltsville group (Borthwick *et al.,* 1952a, 1954). They determined an action spectrum for the promotion by red, which showed maximum activity at about 6500 Å and resembled the light-break action spectra, and also an action spectrum for the infrared (now called far-red) inhibition, which showed a maximum around 7350 Å. More important, however, were observations leading them to postulate the existence of what is now known as the red, far-red reversible pigment system.

Some data taken from the 1954 paper illustrate what is meant by red, far-red reversibility. Groups of lettuce seeds were allowed to imbibe water in darkness at 20° C for three hours, subjected to various brief light treatments, then kept in darkness at 20° C for two days, after which the number germinating in each lot was counted. The light treatments were either 1 minute of red (R) or 4 minutes of far-red (F) at previously established intensities, or combinations of these in immediate succession. In typical results, treatment R alone caused 70 percent germination, and the treatment RF (red followed immediately by far-red) caused 7 percent, almost the same as germination in darkness. Such alternations could be carried much further: the treatment RF, RF, RF, R gave 81 percent, and the treatment RF, RF, RF, RF, 7 percent again. The germination depended simply on whether R or F was given last, as if a switch were thrown one way or the other by the different radiations. Any red effect was reversed by far-red given immediately after, and vice versa. Similar results could be obtained even when the seeds were chilled to 6° C during the period of light treatments. This temperature-independence and a number of other observations led to the suggestion that the two opposed light effects might be mediated by the same pigment. The basic assumption is that the pigment can exist in two forms, a red-absorbing form (or form with greater red than far-red absorption) and a far-red-absorbing form. These two forms, call them P_R and P_F, would be photochemically interconvertible, thus:

$$P_R \xrightleftharpoons[\text{far-red light}]{\text{red light}} P_F,$$

and the final physiological result would then depend on whatever form remained after the last illumination, or on the ratio of the two.

THE RED, FAR-RED SYSTEM IN PHOTOPERIODISM

Evidence for the red, far-red reversibility of photoperiodic light-breaks was presented first by Borthwick et al. (1952b), using *Xanthium*. Following this, Downs (1956) showed that the effects of light-breaks were also far-red reversible in the LDP *Hyoscyamus niger* and Wintex barley and the SDP *Amaranthus caudatus* and Biloxi soybean, and was able to demonstrate repeated reversibility, like that in lettuce seeds, in both *Xanthium* and soybeans. A more concrete account of some of these results may be illustrative at this point.

By this time, simpler light sources than the spectrograph had been developed. The red source was simply white fluorescent light (about 1000 foot candles at plant level) with an interposed filter of two sheets of red cellophane. Far-red was obtained by filtering either sunlight (8000 foot candles) or incandescent light (800 foot candles)—both rich in far-red compared to fluorescent light—through two layers each of red and blue cellophane. These cut out almost all radiation of wavelengths shorter than 7000 Å but allow far-red to pass. Using these sources, Downs then conducted a more detailed investigation of the time and energy relations of these effects on *Xanthium*. Groups of plants were given various experimental treatments for three 24-hour cycles. They were all then placed under noninductive long-day conditions and allowed to develop for some days, after which the flowering response was scored as an inflorescence-stage index from 0 (vegetative) to 7 (maximum response).

The effect of red light in the middle of each dark period of three successive 12 hours·light-12 hours dark cycles was proportional to the duration of exposure, that is, to total energy given.

Uninterrupted controls had a mean flowering stage of 6.0; 10 seconds red gave a value of about 4.8, 20 seconds brought it to about 2.5, and 30 seconds, to 0. One minute of sun-source far-red was sufficient to reverse the effects of two minutes of red if given immediately after, returning the value to 6, but twelve minutes of far-red brought it down again to nearly 4; such "overreversals," in which long exposures to far-red act more like red, occur in other plants as well, and will be discussed later.

Downs next studied the effect of interposing a brief period between the red and far-red treatments. In one experiment, far-red immediately after red gave a value of 6.5 compared with the uninterrupted controls of 7.0. With a 20-minute dark period before the same far-red treatment, the value was only 3.8, and with a 40-minute dark period, 0.5. Thus the far-red treatment had to be given soon after the red to be effective; the simplest explanation is that when most of the pigment is in the far-red-absorbing form (after the red), a series of reactions inhibitory to induction is started and reaches such a stage after 40 minutes that even changing the pigment will no longer change the result. If the plants are held at 5° C during the intervening dark period, this "escape from photochemical control" occurs much more slowly. With a 40-minute dark period, for example, the red effect was still almost completely reversible at this temperature, precisely as would be expected under the explanation given. The escape from photochemical control also explains why, under ordinary conditions, repeated reversals cannot be carried on indefinitely and the red effect eventually predominates.

Downs's results typify the kind of control exerted by the red, far-red system in photoperiodism, but by no means exhaust the subject. Evidence was obtained, first in lettuce seed (Borthwick et al., 1952a) and later elsewhere, that the conversion from the far-red-absorbing to the red-absorbing form takes place not only on exposure to far-red but also, more slowly, in darkness by some thermal (temperature-dependent) process. This revises the relation previously written to:

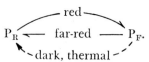

Certain data on flowering further suggested that this dark conversion might determine the length of the critical dark period. Borthwick *et al.* (1952b) reported that if *Xanthium* plants were given a brief far-red exposure at the beginning of a dark period (end of the high-intensity white light), less than 7 hours of darkness were required for induction. If they received a brief red treatment instead, 9 hours of darkness were required, compared with the 8½ sufficient with no treatment after the white light. Downs (1959) has also shown that the quantitative SDP millet, *Setaria italica*, which flowers rapidly with 12-hour nights but very slowly with 8-hour nights, will also flower rapidly with 8-hour nights if a brief far-red treatment is given at the beginning of each. This far-red promotion of flowering is reversed by red, and red alone has no effect at the start of the dark periods. (See Fig. 3-3.)

At this point one may well wish for the solace of a theory unifying all these data. Such a theory exists (see Borthwick, Hendricks, and Parker, 1956) and can be briefly summarized. At the end of a long white-light period, the pigment is almost completely in the far-red-absorbing form; evidence for this is that red given then has little or no effect, and far-red a much larger one. It is this far-red-absorbing form that brings about the inhibition of induction in SDP and the promotion of induction in LDP. Thus SDP require a dark period long enough to allow thermal conversion of the far-red-absorbing form and its continued absence for some time, whereas LDP are inhibited by too long a dark period since this conversion and absence are unfavorable. Hence red (or white) light-breaks inhibit SDP induction and promote LDP induction by returning the pigment to the far-red-absorbing form. This theory takes into account all the data so far presented, and even fits the observation (Chapter Two) that the dark period for *Xanthium* has to be longer if the temperature is lowered, since thermal conversion to the red-absorbing form will be slowed. The only difficulty is that it does not fit the equally valid data to be considered next.

According to the theory, far-red given to LDP at the start of a dark period barely short enough to allow induction should inhibit induction. Yet in at least two LDP, *Hyoscyamus* and dill, it promoted induction. Also, flowering in the SDP *Chrysanthemum morifolium* is not promoted by far-red at the start of the dark period, as it is in *Xanthium* and millet (see Borthwick, 1959). Still more complicated, yet confirmed now by the Beltsville group whose theory it confounds, is the response of the Japanese morning glory, *Pharbitis nil.*

Fig. 3-3. Effect of far-red supplement at the end of the light period on the SDP millet (*Setaria italica*). All plants were grown with 16 hours of light; at the end of each light period the following treatments were given, represented by the plants from left to right: no further radiation; five minutes of far-red; five minutes of far-red followed by five minutes of red. (Photograph from Downs [1959], by permission of the American Association for the Advancement of Science, and courtesy of Drs. R. J. Downs and H. A. Borthwick, U. S. Department of Agriculture.)

Pharbitis seedlings grown at about 26° C can be induced to flower by one or more 16-hour dark periods, and red light-breaks (perceived by the cotyledons) 8 or 10 hours after the start of the dark period completely inhibit induction. This is a typical SDP response. But the effects of red light are not reversed by far-red; far-red itself inhibits flowering when given during the dark period. Far-red even inhibits when given at the start of the dark period, and *this* effect is reversed by red. Thus the red, far-red reversible system is present and active, but in a way unlike that suggested by the theory (Nakayama, 1958). However, all this is true only when the cotyledons are the light-responsive organs. Older plants, in which the true leaves perceive the light, respond in the same way as *Xanthium* (Nakayama, Borthwick, and Hendricks, 1960). These observations provide an opportunity for studying the precise ways in which the red, far-red system may be linked to flowering, if the operative differences between the cotyledons and the true leaves can be discovered.

A point requiring further comment is that white light acts more or less like red. This is not surprising for fluorescent light sources since their far-red emission is very low, but both incandescent light and sunlight have a high proportion of far-red. Their action as red light is probably due in part to the proportion of red to far-red, in part to the relative sensitivities of the two forms, and also to the fact, mentioned previously, that prolonged exposures to far-red may have an action more like red than short exposures. The latter has been explained (see Borthwick, 1959) as being due to the maintenance of a small amount of the far-red-absorbing form in equilibrium with the red-absorbing form during far-red radiation, since the absorption spectra of the two forms must overlap. Thus darkness following the far-red treatment is needed to allow the conversion to the red-absorbing form to be completed by the thermal process. It is, however, not strictly true that all white light sources are equivalent for photoperiodism. Fluorescent and incandescent light differ considerably in their effects on both flowering and vegetative growth when used to lengthen light periods, and the differences can be ascribed to the different far-red emissions of the two sources (Downs, 1959; Downs *et al.*, 1959).

NATURE AND FUNCTION OF THE RED, FAR-RED PIGMENT

Many effects of low-intensity red light on plants are now known to be reversible by far-red, but a discussion of the red, far-red control of vegetative growth—so-called photomorphogenesis—would occupy too much space here. References to the abundant literature on it are to be found in most reviews on photoperiodism; a particularly good introduction is Withrow's own article in Withrow (1959). Much speculation and calculation has in the past been devoted to the possible nature and metabolic function of such a reversible pigment system, on the assumption, of course, that it existed and was not a misinterpretation of two separate light effects. The assumption has since been justified, and the speculations may soon give way to data. Workers at Beltsville (Butler *et al.,* 1959), using relatively sophisticated spectrophotometric techniques, have shown that intact tissues and properly prepared extracts of etiolated (dark-grown) seedlings of various species, such as corn, *Zea mays,* contain a pigment with the predicted reversible changes in absorption characteristics in the red and far-red. The pigment is present in very low concentrations—the etiolated tissue in which it was observed was nearly white—and is either a protein or closely bound to a protein. The development of better extraction and purification techniques should soon make it possible to characterize the pigment further and aid in establishing its immediate biochemical function. The rapid developments which should ensue may make further discussion on these points obsolete when printed.

Even discovery of the immediate biochemical function of the pigment, no easy matter in itself, will not completely clarify its role in photoperiodism. Much more physiological work is still required on this question. The only generalization that will hold at present is that the red, far-red system mediates the low-intensity light effects and may also be involved in the critical time-requirements. There is no clear evidence, however, as to the precise way in which the pigment is linked to subsequent events in the induction process, and the relation may well differ from species to species even within a given response class.

The pigment has been dubbed "phytochrome" by its discoverers (see Borthwick and Hendricks, 1960). Though the name is unfortunate both because it is general (Greek for "plant" plus "color" or "pigment") and because it is liable to be confused when spoken with the cytochromes, so significant in the biochemistry of respiration, it will undoubtedly be perpetuated.

PROLONGED EXPOSURES TO LIGHT OF DIFFERENT COLORS

In the 1930's and 1940's, Funke (see Funke, 1948) used sunlight filtered through white, red, or blue glass to lengthen photoperiods for both LDP and SDP. Red and white were the only effective photoperiod-lengthening conditions for many, with blue equivalent to darkness. For a second large class, both red and blue were effective, as well as white. For a third very small class, only white was effective, but neither red nor blue. Funke's "Class IV" has attracted the most interest; these were all of the Cruciferae (Mustard family) and almost all LDP, in which the blue and white, but not the red, were effective in lengthening photoperiod.

Since Funke, there has been a great deal of work, most of it in the Netherlands, on the vegetative development and flowering of plants grown with relatively high energies (high intensities, long exposures, or both) of various colors of light. For reviews of this work, see Wassink and Stolwijk (1956), Wassink *et al.* (1959), Meijer (1959), and Van der Veen and Meijer (1959). Although many interesting phenomena have been observed, such work is, almost without exception, extremely difficult to evaluate for at least two reasons. First is the immense technical difficulty of obtaining high energies of light in pure spectral bands and over large enough areas to grow groups of whole plants. Often the sources have been more or less impure, as Funke's must have been, so that what appear to be high-energy effects of the main wavelength region may include low-energy effects of other wavelengths. Such contaminations have been gradually reduced (see Wassink *et al.*, 1959) but may still be present. The second problem is, if anything, worse. Consider, for example, the effects of long exposure to high-intensity blue light, no matter how pure. The light may be affecting at least three systems simultaneously. The red, far-red system itself and photosynthesis are already obvious, but one must also consider whatever pigments mediate phototropism—the orientation of plant parts with respect to the direction of light—since blue light is the most effective in this process. In addition, fluorescence of chlorophyll and other compounds caused by the blue may expose the cells internally to longer-wave radiations. The difficulties of disentangling such effects and reaching satisfactory interpretations can hardly be overestimated. Nevertheless, some of this work is of considerable interest.

The unexpected promotion of *Hyoscyamus* flowering by farred at the start of the dark period, mentioned above, was first reported by Stolwijk and Zeevaart (1955) who also observed that this LDP entirely failed to flower when grown in continuous red light, although it flowers rapidly in continuous white light. However, small amounts of far-red given with the continuous red brought about flowering, as did also blue light. Nine hours of blue once every third day would permit flowering under otherwise continuous red light. There is some question as to whether the slight far-red contamination in the blue might be responsible for the original effect reported, but it has since been repeated with much purer sources (Wassink *et al.,* 1959). Thus, in *Hyoscyamus,* blue and far-red may be physiologically equivalent for flower initiation.

Meijer (1959) has reported a number of complex experiments on flower initiation in the SDP *Salvia occidentalis.* One of the most interesting results is that a standard 15-minute red light-break during an inductive dark period does not inhibit flowering if the main (8-hour) light period is of red or green light. It does inhibit, however, if the main light period is of blue (all main light periods being of the same energy) or if the red or green periods are supplemented with far-red. It should also be noted that *Salvia occidentalis,* like *Perilla crispa* (Chapter Two) will flower even in continuous white light of sufficiently low intensities; at higher or even lower intensities, it again behaves like a proper SDP by failing to flower. Even more complex work on *Hyoscyamus* has been recently reported by De Lint (1960), to whose extensive work the reader should go for further details.

Work of this kind has certainly indicated that light quality and intensity have more effects on flower initiation and other aspects of development than can readily be explained through what is known of the red, far-red system at present. Unfortunately, even the effects of blue on this particular system are not understood; there is evidence that, in various organisms, blue (at high energies) may act like either red or far-red. Whether this is a direct action on the red, far-red reversible pigment itself or an indirect one, through other pigments or metabolic systems, is uncertain. Due to the difficulties, already mentioned, of interpreting such studies, the only suggestions at present are purely speculative.

B. TIME RELATIONS AND ENDOGENOUS RHYTHMS IN PHOTOPERIODISM

The characteristic defining aspect of photoperiodism is the importance of the time relations of light and dark conditions. The response to this timing is sometimes surprisingly precise; *Xanthium* can distinguish clearly between a dark period of 8 hours (non-inductive) and one of 8 hours, 40 minutes (inductive) (Long, 1939). On the reasonable assumption that the main survival value of photoperiodism in an organism is in the seasonal timing of development that it affords, Withrow (1959) has calculated that to be accurate, the timing mechanism must detect daylength differences of 14 to 44 minutes within a week in temperate latitudes. In addition, it should be relatively insensitive to random changes in light intensity and temperature brought about by local weather. Insensitivity to intensity changes is provided by the fact that low intensities are sufficient to bring about most photoperiodic responses, but insensitivity to temperature is more difficult to understand. Although both the accuracy and the temperature-insensitivity (see Chapter Two) of the photoperiodic control of flowering are, in the writer's opinion, often exaggerated, it is true that certain aspects of photoperiodism are less temperature-sensitive than most plant processes.

The effects of low temperature in lengthening the critical dark period in *Xanthium,* discussed earlier, indicate that a drop of about 16° C increased the dark period required by only about 3 hours, or less than 40 percent (Long, 1939). This contrasts with the general observation that the rates of most ordinary chemical reactions, and thus of growth or other processes in most biological systems, are at least doubled by a 10° C rise in temperature within a fairly wide range. If the series of events constituting the dark period "timing mechanism" in *Xanthium* responded in this fashion, one would expect the 16° drop in temperature to bring about at least a 20- or 24-hour dark requirement, but it does not. This and similar evidence, although there is not a great deal of it, suggest that the photoperodic timing mechanism is not a simple linear series of ordinary reactions, but may be more complex.

Neither timing nor temperature-insensitivity are peculiar to photoperiodism. In mammals and birds, of course, a self-regulated temperature could obviously permit the accurate timing of responses and metabolic events by simple chemical means alone, but it is now well established that probably all plants and animals—even unicells, excluding perhaps the bacteria—have accurate timing mechanisms that are temperature-insensitive, more so, in fact, than most photoperiodic phenomena. Several groups of workers have thus suggested that photoperiodism, in both plants and animals, is merely a special case of a general rhythmic mechanism by which all organisms can register the passage of time.

ENDOGENOUS CIRCADIAN RHYTHMS IN PLANTS

Most of the recent data on rhythmic processes in higher plants have come either from Erwin Bünning and his co-workers in Germany or from work done elsewhere to test their hypotheses. Bünning's concepts (see Bünning, 1956, 1959) have developed from a number of basic observations, some antedating his own work.

Most plant processes exhibit a diurnal rhythm in phase with the daily alternations of light and darkness. This rhythm is not simply a passive response to external conditions since as expressed in various processes—the nocturnal "sleep" movements of legume leaves, for example—it persists for at least a few days after the plants are placed in a constant-temperature dark room. In fact, periodic light-dark alternations are not necessary to initiate such a rhythm. The classic example is the behavior of bean, *Phaseolus*, seedlings germinated and grown in constant-temperature darkness. The movements of the young leaves, which can be recorded with a suitable apparatus, are small, more or less random, and unsynchronized among the population of seedlings. After a single flash of light the movements become larger, synchronized among all the seedlings, and exhibit a marked periodicity, with the leaves returning to the same position about once every 24 hours. The movements become weaker after several days and finally die out, but maintain their periodicity until they do. In Bünning's view, such results provide evidence of "endogenous daily rhythms" in plants.

By "endogenous" Bünning means that the period, or length of a complete oscillation in such rhythms, is determined by the plant and not imposed by external conditions. There are at least three kinds of evidence for this in experiments with the leaf movements of bean seedlings. First, of course, the movements are evoked by a single exposure to light, not by a repeated light-dark schedule. Second, the phase of the rhythm—as indicated by the position of a leaf at any given time—is not affected by the solar time of day, but depends only on the time at which the light flash was given. A group of plants given a flash 12 hours before a second group will show movements 12 hours out of phase with the second group. Finally, and perhaps most important, the rhythm of such movements is not exactly daily, not precisely 24 hours long. It may be from 20 to 30 hours; different varieties have rhythms with characteristic period-lengths, so that this is a genetically controlled and thus endogenous property. The term "circadian" (Latin: *circa,* about, and *dies,* day) has been coined for such rhythms with period-lengths of close to 24 hours.

The relation of the bean circadian rhythm to temperature is shown by data from Bünning (1959a). In darkness (after a light flash) the period is 28.3 hours at constant 15° C and 28.0 hours at constant 25° C. Thus a 10° difference in ambient temperature has no effect. However, a change in temperature does have an effect. Seedlings moved from 20° to 15° had a period of 29.7 hours, and those moved from 20° to 25° had a period of 23.7 hours, for the first day or so after a change. Later, compensation occurred and the periods in the two temperatures became similar. Thus it is not strictly true to call such circadian rhythms temperature-insensitive, but they are clearly temperature-compensated and arrive at the same period in different constant temperatures.

In general, the phase and amplitude of circadian rhythms in various organisms are greatly affected by the environment but the basic period-length can only be changed within narrow limits. An organism with a rhythm of 20 or 30 hours will adapt its period to a normal 24-hour day, but may either revert to its endogenous rhythm or exhibit highly disorganized activity under light-dark cycles totaling 12 hours in length. Not only light flashes but transitions from light to darkness and abrupt temperature shocks as well can reset the phase or initiate circadian rhythms, but it seems clear that they do not cause them.

Many processes in an organism generally exhibit the same circadian rhythm, probably manifesting the activity of a single "clock" mechanism. This "clock" may be a basic property of the organization of most cells or a particular unknown process, but there is no general agreement even as to its possible nature. A major investigator (Brown, 1959) has recently abandoned the hypothesis of a completely endogenous origin, and suggests that organisms may register the passage of time by perceiving certain unknown geophysical periodicities, although the way in which such an exogenous clock may be used would still vary greatly from organism to organism. Most other workers, however, consider the clock truly endogenous. For summaries of the state of this field with particular reference to animals and microörganisms, see Pittendrigh and Bruce (1959) and Brown (1959); a recent symposium also covers the field in great detail (*Biological Clocks,* 1960). Only experiments directly concerned with photoperiodism and flowering will be considered below.

ENDOGENOUS CIRCADIAN RHYTHMS AS THE BASIS OF PHOTOPERIODISM

In the view of Bünning and co-workers, the endogenous circadian rhythm of plants passes through two phases of more or less opposite sensitivity to light: a "photophile" (light-liking) phase in which development is favored by light and a "scotophile" (dark-liking) phase in which light is unfavorable. These phases are said to be distinguishable by leaf movements as well as by differences in rates of respiration, photosynthesis, cell division, and other processes. As phases of a circadian rhythm they are affected but not caused by light-dark alternations; they are the means by which the plant can "time" the light or dark exposures it receives. A particular version of this view, now considerably modified by Bünning (1948, 1959b), has provided the stimulus for much of the work on the problem. It relates SDP and LDP specifically by proposing that in both types each phase of the rhythm is about 12 hours long, but whereas in SDP the photophile normally starts soon after illumination, in LDP it starts only some 8 to 12 hours after the start of light. Thus long photoperiods give the SDP excessive light in its scotophile, whereas short photoperiods give LDP most of the light in the scotophile and little in the photophile.

An example of the kind of evidence supporting this proposal is from Bünning and Kemmler (1954). They found that flowering in the LDP dill occurred on a daily schedule of $17\frac{1}{2}$ hours light-$6\frac{1}{2}$ hours darkness, but was more rapid if a 2-hour dark period was given 3 hours after the start of each main light period (making the schedule 3 hours light-2 hours dark-$12\frac{1}{2}$ hours light-$6\frac{1}{2}$ hours dark). This observation is consistent with the idea that dill has a scotophile phase that occurs shortly after the start of the main light period, and thus darkness during this time promotes flowering. However, the effect was not detected in the LDP *Plantago* and spinach.

Evidence has also been obtained from leaf movements, a particularly impressive case being that of *Madia elegans*. This desert composite was first studied by Lewis and Went (1945) who found that it flowered rapidly with 8, 18, or 24 hours of light per day, but slowly with 12 or 14 hours of light. This unusual bimodal sensitivity, with intermediate daylengths less effective than long or short, is apparently reflected in the leaf movements. Bünning (1951) was able to show that these movements corresponded to what his hypothesis would predict for a plant with two photophile phases within each circadian period, and he explained the peculiar photoperiodic response on this basis. Indeed, leaf movements have generally been used as the chief indication of the postulated phase changes. Those in various soybeans, for example, can indicate whether a given variety will show SDP or daylength-indifferent flowering responses (Bünning, 1955). Although leaf movements in *Kalanchoë* are difficult to detect, Schwemmle (1957) has found that the effects of high temperature given at various times during inductive dark periods (see Chapter Two) are well correlated with the effects of similar treatments on the rhythmic movements of the petals of plants in flower. Not all the leaf-movement work is so favorable, however; there is apparently no significant difference between the rhythmic leaf movements of the qualitative SDP *Coleus frederici* and *Coleus frederici* x *blumei* and those of the quantitative LDP *Coleus blumei* (Kribben, 1955). At best, of course, correlatory evidence is merely circumstantial, whether favorable or unfavorable.

CIRCADIAN RHYTHMS AND THE ACTION OF LIGHT-BREAKS

The most widely used tool in assessing the relation of circadian rhythms to photoperiodism, as in the study of low-intensity light processes, has been the light-break. Here, instead of quality and intensity, the timing of the light-breaks and the length of the dark periods are the factors varied. It was tacitly assumed during the preceding sections that light-breaks are most effective when given in the middle of the dark period. This is very approximately true in ordinary 24-hour cycles, but rarely so under other conditions, as such work has made evident. Under the rhythm hypothesis, light-breaks act not by merely breaking each long dark period into two short ones, but by supplying light in the scotophile (for SDP) or photophile (for LDP) phases. This has been tested extensively.

When Claes and Lang (1947) examined the effects of 48-hour cycles on *Hyoscyamus* (Chapter Two), they found that cycles of 7 hours light-41 hours darkness were noninductive. A 2-hour light-break would promote flowering if given not long after the start or before the end of each long dark period, but was ineffective in the middle. The times of maximum effectiveness were about 16 and 40 hours, respectively, after the start of each main light period. These results were consistent with the idea that the photophile-scotophile alternation continued through the dark period with the first photophile maximum (typical of LDP) 16 hours after the start of the main light period and the second about 24 hours after the first. Yet there was an equally reasonable alternative explanation not depending on rhythms. Suppose that the light-break could act together with the main light period nearest it (either before or after) to constitute a long light period interrupted (without effect) by darkness. On this alternative the light-break was ineffective in the middle of the long dark period not because it fell in the scoto-phile, as in the rhythm explanation, but because it was too far from a main light period. Claes and Lang favored the second view.

An experiment designed to avoid this ambiguity was reported by Carr (1952), who used the SDP *Kalanchoë* grown in 72-hour cycles of 12 hours light-60 hours darkness. On the Bünning theory, light-breaks during the dark period should show *three* times of maximum effectiveness in inhibiting flowering and causing the correlated changes in vegetative growth, whereas on the Claes and Lang alternative there should be only two, close to either end of the dark period. Carr's results indeed showed three maxima, about 24 hours apart, although the middle one was not as well defined as one might wish. Carr concluded that "the theory of Bünning . . . must therefore be regarded as finally and decisively proved," thereby illustrating the partisan vigor that at least enlivens if not clarifies the question.

Schwabe (1955a) repeated Carr's results but noted that the

crucial differences (evidence for the second, or middle, maximum) were very small, and reached opposite conclusions on other grounds (see below); but very clear data confirming Carr's results were later published by Melchers (1956). Meanwhile, Hussey (1954) had shown that the LDP *Anagallis arvensis* grown in 72-hour cycles with long dark periods showed only two maxima for the promotion of flowering by light-breaks instead of the three that would correspond to Carr's results. With *Hyoscyamus*, however, Clauss and Rau (1956) were able to show three optima in similar experiments, thus supporting Carr and Bünning. The quantitative LDP *Arabidopsis thaliana* was studied twice, with ambiguous results each time (Hussey, 1954; Clauss and Rau, 1956). The SDP *Coleus blumei* x *frederici* disagreed with all others, since the time for maximum light-break inhibition (72-hour cycle) was in the middle of the long dark period, with no sign of three or even two optima (Kribben, 1955).

Other work besides that on 72-hour cycles suggests Carr's quoted conclusion may have been hasty. Wareing (1954) voiced strong opposition to the idea that endogenous alternation of photophile and scotophile phases determines the action of light-breaks. He presented experiments with Biloxi soybeans grown on 9 hours light-39 hours darkness (48-hour cycles), or on 9 hours light-51 hours darkness (60-hour cycles), testing the effects of light-breaks at various times during the long dark periods. In both cycles light-breaks about 6 to 8 hours before or after the main light periods were maximally inhibitory, whereas they promoted flowering in the middle of the dark periods. Since the dark periods used in the two cycles differed by 12 hours, one would not expect these results if the inhibitory action of light-breaks was due to a more or less unchanged circadian rhythm. One would expect them, however, if light-breaks interact with the main photoperiod when it is close enough, thus providing a total photoperiod that exceeds the "limiting value" for soybean flowering (see Chapter Two). Further evidence for this view was that in cycles totaling 48 hours, light-breaks given either 3 or 6 hours before the main light period were inhibitory when the latter was 9 hours long, whereas only a light-break 6 hours before was effective with a 6-hour main photoperiod.

Wareing also reported experiments with *Xanthium* in which light-breaks toward the end of a long dark period were not inhibitory. Since this plant, unlike soybeans, has no "limiting photoperiod," these results were consistent with the explanation proposed. The inhibition of *Xanthium* induction by light-breaks given *early* in long dark periods was explained as due to a direct nullification of dark processes leading to flowering plus the fact that, after the light-break, the high-intensity light process (Chapter Two) is left unsatisfied. The induction of *Xanthium* by a critical dark period, regardless of length of the preceding photoperiod, was also cited by Wareing against Bünning's theory, since the latter appeared to hold that the phase of the rhythm was regulated by the start of each main light period. Thus the effect of a dark period should depend on how long the light continued.

Bünning responded to all this in considerable detail. As to the *Xanthium* results, leaf-movement studies (Bünning, 1955) indicated that in this plant the phase of the circadian rhythm is indeed regulated by the light-to-dark rather than the dark-to-light transition, thus refuting Wareing's evidence based on the opposite assumption. A light-break given early in the dark period falls in the scotophile induced by the transition to darkness and thus inhibits, but a light-break late in a long dark period falls in the photophile that endogenously follows and thus does not inhibit. The results with soybeans may also be clarified, according to Bünning (1954), by attention to the actual course of the circadian rhythm as shown by leaf movements. These indicate that the rhythm continues for about 30 hours in darkness, after which a period of "dark rigor" (*Dunkelstarr*) sets in. A light-break during dark rigor brings about a new photophile phase which is then followed endogenously by a scotophile. Wareing's observation that the effect of a light-break toward the end of a long dark period depended not on the length of the dark period but on the light-break's relation to the following main light period is then due to the fact that the main light period and the scotophile phase of the newly reinitiated rhythm now overlap, with resultant inhibition. In addition, Bünning pointed out that his observations on leaf movements would also predict the existence and optimum times for the light-break promotions of flowering observed by Wareing. To Wareing's position that light-break effects are due to interaction with nearby light periods, Bünning thus retorted: "Yes, that is so—because of the endogenous daily rhythm."[1]

---

[1] "Ja, das ist so, und es beruht auf der endogenen Tagesrhythmik."

FLOWERING IN LIGHT-DARK CYCLES OF DIFFERENT
LENGTHS; TEMPERATURE INTERACTIONS

If a circadian rhythm regulates photoperiodic responses, normal flowering should depend upon light-dark alternations of about 24 hours. Schmitz (1951) using *Kalanchoë* and Schwabe (1955a) using *Kalanchoë, Xanthium,* and an SDP variety of *Impatiens balsamina,* concluded against Bünning's theory on the grounds that cycles with total lengths ranging from 15 to 50 hours proved inductive, with any failures to flower attributable to the length of either the dark or light periods but not to the periodicity of the cycles. Schwabe also criticized the extensive use of leaf-movements as indicators of the endogenous rhythm, since the photoperiodic response is often insensitive to conditions which may completely obscure the leaf movements. Calling attention to the remarkable plasticity of both the endogenous rhythm and Bünning's theory based on it, Schwabe questioned the value of the latter in explaining photoperiodism and asked Bünning to "define the sort of experimental result which he would regard as incompatible with it."

In contrast to the results of Schmitz and Schwabe, cycle-length experiments show clear quantitative effects on the flowering of soybeans (Blaney and Hamner, 1957; Nanda and Hamner, 1958, 1959). Cycles totaling 24, 48, or 72 hours in length are far more favorable to flowering than, for example, 36- or 60-hour cycles, although neither of these most unfavorable cycles are completely inhibitory. This certainly supports the concept of a circadian rhythm in sensitivity to light and darkness. Finn and Hamner (1960) have also published a group of experiments with *Hyoscyamus* in which the total length of the light-dark cycle appears to be a major controlling factor. For example, with a 10-hour light period, flowering was most rapid with a total cycle length of 18 hours (with an 8-hour dark period), slowest or absent with a total cycle length of 24–30 hours (14- or 20-hour dark period), and faster again with a 42-hour cycle length (32-hour dark period). Such results may also be used to support a rhythm-based theory of photoperiodism.

Further experiments with soybeans (Blaney and Hamner, 1957)

indicate that the phase of the rhythm can be shifted by low temperatures during part of the cycles used. A recent paper by Oltmanns (1960) suggests that the interactions between temperature, light, and rhythmic phemonena in the flowering of *Kalanchoë*, and by implication in the flowering of any other plant, are not yet sufficiently understood to be described by any simple hypothesis.

ENDOGENOUS CIRCADIAN RHYTHMS AND THE RED, FAR-RED SYSTEM

There appears to be a relationship between the red, far-red system, unquestionably involved in photoperiodism, and endogenous circadian rhythms in plants. Red is the most effective light in initiating the movements of etiolated bean seedlings, previously discussed, and this effect is far-red reversible (see Bünning, 1959a). More directly related to photoperiodism is the observation by Könitz (1958) that far-red given as an interruption of the main light period of *Chenopodium amaranticolor* (SDP) inhibits the effectiveness of inductive cycles, just as does red given in the dark period. Since rhythms in plants demonstrably affect many processes under certain circumstances, the particular closeness of their connection with the red, far-red system is hard to judge, even from these results. Engelmann (1960) has found that when red light is given to *Kalanchoë* at various times during a 62-hour dark period, it inhibits induction in what would be predicted to be the scotophile phases and promotes it in the photophile phases. Far-red, however, does not show an inverse pattern, but simply inhibits during the first half (30 hours) of each dark period and inhibits less during the second half.

CONCLUDING REMARKS ON CIRCADIAN RHYTHMS AND PHOTOPERIODISM

If the reader is now confused, he is in good company; no aspect of flowering physiology has given rise to more complex experiments, tenuous interpretations, and heated controversy. The controversy is not over the existence of rhythms in plants, which is not seriously questioned, but over their usefulness and relevance in understanding photoperiodism. In this situation, even more obviously than in most, appeals to expert opinion are useless, since there are accomplished and respected investigators on both sides. The writer is frankly of two minds on the subject. On the one hand, the existence of rhythms and their influence in many processes recommend them as the underlying mechanism of the more particular time-dependent response, photoperiodism. Yet hypotheses on the precise relationship tend to seem vague, or easily disproved, or *ad hoc* elaborations full of special exceptions. It has understandably been argued that they simply confuse the issue, explaining the relatively simple response of photoperiodism in terms of an equally unexplained set of more complex phenomena. Yet, if photoperiodism is indeed a special case of a basic biological process, it would be a pity not to recognize it as such. So far, the evidence on both sides consists largely of correlations or the lack of correlations, and these differ from plant to plant. Certainly endogenous circadian rhythms are at least modifying factors in photoperiodism; whether they are more than that, time will undoubtedly tell.

chapter four $\blacktriangleright$ Temperature

and Flowering

Temperature affects all plant processes, and some temperature interactions with photoperiodism have already been mentioned. There are many plants in which flowering is either qualitatively or quantitatively dependent upon exposure to near-freezing temperatures, and it is largely with these that this chapter will deal. A few other less well-defined relationships between temperature and flowering will also be considered.

VERNALIZATION: COLD TREATMENTS AND FLOWERING

It is evident from Chapter Two that photoperiodism provides not only a convenient method for controlling and studying flowering in many plants, but also a basis for the explanation of many seasonal phenomena. The same is true of low-temperature effects, which play an important role in the life cycles of many temperate-zone plants. Among the monocarpic plants, both biennials and winter annuals are forms in which a cold treatment is required before flowering can take place with optimum rapidity; in winter annuals it can be given during germination to very young seedlings, whereas biennials must first have made substantial growth. Many perennials also, both woody and herbaceous, require cold treatments each season to continue flowering. The ecological and adap-

54

tive significance of such behavior in regions with a period of winter cold, itself unfavorable to growth, need not be belabored.

The cold treatment of germinating seeds in order to hasten subsequent flowering has come to be known as *vernalization*. This is a translation of the Russian *yarovizatsya*, and both words combine the term for "spring" (Russian, *yarov*; Latin, *ver*) with a suffix implying "to make" or "become," reflecting the ability of such cold treatments to convert "winter" strains of cereals to the "spring" habit by satisfying their cold requirement. Winter cereals must normally be planted in late fall or winter in order to flower and produce a crop in the subsequent year, whereas spring varieties may be planted in the spring of the year in which the crop is expected. The terms vernalization or yarovizatsya both actually postdate the first observations of such effects by many years, but it was Russian attention to the possible practical values of the process, particularly in the 1930's, that brought it generally to world-wide notice. For the history of early work on vernalization, see McKinney (1940) and Whyte (1948).

Vernalization is probably the only aspect of plant physiology that ever became involved in political ideology. The agronomic use of vernalization in the Soviet Union was popularized by T. D. Lysenko, who viewed the effect as an actual inheritable conversion from winter to spring habit; later he even claimed the conversion of one species of wheat into another. Lysenko's theory eventually led to the establishment of a Marxist form of Lamarckism—an old and thoroughly discredited view, which holds that changes produced by the environment are directly inherited by the offspring of the changed organism—as the Soviet dogma in biology. The adopting of this view by the Soviets was probably partly due to simple opportunism on Lysenko's part, as he was its chief interpreter. Some of the finest biologists in the U.S.S.R. refused to support the official line and, as a result, simply disappeared or were demoted. This unfortunate episode in the history of science has been recounted and analyzed by Huxley (1949) and Zirkle (1949) but does not appear to have run its course even yet, so that Soviet biology still labors under a disadvantage. Ironically, vernalization has not proved to be of great agronomic importance, since the breeding of varieties suitable for particular climates and uses has been far more successful. At present, the chief practical applications of an understanding of such low-temperature effects are in relatively small-scale horticultural and floricultural practices.

Vernalization in winter rye

Although accounts of the effects of chilling seeds and seedlings abound in the literature, there have been relatively few extensive studies of vernalization. The work of F. G. Gregory, O. N. Purvis, and their collaborators in England since about 1931, on the effects of vernalization and photoperiodism on flower initiation, development, and vegetative growth of spring and winter strains of the Petkus variety of rye, *Secale cereale,* is by far the most thorough.

The spring strain is a typical quantitative LDP. Under sufficiently long days, flower initiation begins after approximately seven leaves have differentiated, whereas under short days (10 hours light) it occurs only after at least 22 leaves have been produced. The winter strain, when germinated at relatively high temperatures (for example, 18° C), is not an LDP, but flowers equally slowly—again after about 22 leaves—under both long and short days. However, if the germinating winter strain is vernalized by holding it at 1° C for several weeks before planting, it subsequently responds to long days in the same way as does the spring strain (Purvis, 1934). The effect of vernalization is thus to render the seedling sensitive to long days; early flower initiation does not take place as a result of vernalization alone, or vernalization followed by short days.

The effect of vernalization is proportional, within limits, to the duration of the cold treatment. Four days' exposure is sufficient to increase the subsequent relative growth rate of the stem apex, but has no effect on either the number of days from planting to full anthesis or the number of leaves preceding flower initiation. Both values are reduced to a minimum (under subsequent long days) by increasing the length of the cold treatment up to 14 weeks (Purvis and Gregory, 1937).

To determine what portion of the germinating seed perceives the cold treatment, Gregory and Purvis (1938a) and Purvis (1940) studied the effects of low temperature on excised intact embryos and parts of embryos. Not only the intact embryo itself, separated from the rest of the seed, but even its isolated apex alone are susceptible to vernalization, giving rise to plants responding optimally to long days. Thus the site of vernalization is in the meristem itself, and the results of vernalization are somehow maintained throughout the development of the plant derived from the few cells originally exposed. The technique of vernalizing isolated embryos also made it possible to show that vernalization requires a carbohydrate source, presumably as an energy supply for the process involved. Rapid flowering takes place only if the embryos are cold-treated on a medium containing sucrose, although subsequent vegetative growth is excellent even if the medium consists of mineral salts alone (Gregory and DeRopp, 1938).

Oxygen is also required during vernalization, confirming the suggestion that the process requires a considerable amount of energy. For example, Gregory and Purvis (1938b) found that germinating seeds held at 1° C for 9 weeks would eventually produce inflorescences after the eighth leaf if the cold treatment was given in air, but only after the twenty-third, as in the unvernalized controls, if the treatment was in nitrogen. As little as 1/500 of the normal air concentration of oxygen allowed some vernalization to take place, but not the maximum effect.

Before proceeding further, one should bear in mind that confusion occasionally arises between vernalization and the favorable effects of chilling on seed germination in many species. The former has relatively specific effects, inductive in the sense that they lead to subsequent changes in the flowering response of the plants. Mere cold treatment to hasten germination is not necessarily vernalization. It may indeed result in earlier flowering, but the use of developmental criteria (number of leaves before the inflorescence, for example) can usually indicate whether a genuine hastening of flowering relative to vegetative growth has occurred.

Vernalization in other plants

The flowering not only of winter cereal strains, but of many other plants, can be hastened by vernalization. Certain varieties of peas, *Pisum sativum,* can be made to produce their first flower at an earlier node. In the variety Zelka, the eighteenth or nineteenth nodes are the first to bear flowers if germination and growth take place at about 20° C, but if the germinating seeds are kept at 7° for 30 days before planting, flowers occur beginning with the fourteenth or fifteenth nodes. The physiological stage susceptible to vernalization appears to be very brief. If the germinating seeds are kept at 20° for 3 days or at 26° for 1 or 2 days, they can no longer be vernalized, even though no new nodes have developed during the short time involved (Highkin, 1956).

The term vernalization has been extended to cover similar effects of low temperature given not to germinating seeds but to already developed plants. Such effects are typically found in biennials and many perennials, and are at least formally similar to those obtained with the very young plants used in "true" vernalization. One plant frequently studied is the biennial strain of *Hyoscyamus niger,* previously introduced as an LDP. The strain discussed in Chapters Two and Three was the annual, from which the biennial appears to differ only in having a cold (vernalization) requirement. After this requirement is satisfied, it responds to daylength in the same way as the annual strain, but it cannot flower otherwise. It thus shows a qualitative vernalization requirement, unlike the plants so far discussed.

Some of Lang's (1951) results with biennial *Hyoscyamus* illustrate how vernalization depends on both the temperature and duration of exposure. Plants were exposed to temperatures from 3° to 17° C under 8-hour day conditions for varying periods of time, after which they were placed in 16-hour days at 23° C. The vernalizing effectiveness of the various temperature treatments was then expressed by the time required under long days before flower initiation was detectable; the shorter the time, the more effective the vernalization. With a vernalizing time of 105 days, all temperatures from 3° to 14° were highly effective: flower initiation was detected after 8 days under the long-day conditions. With only 15 days of vernalization, 10° was the most effective temperature, giving 23 days to initiation as compared to the 35 days given by 3° and the 28 days given by 14°. With an intermediate vernalizing time of 42 days, both 3° and 6° allowed initiation after 10 long days; 17° gave initiation after 20, and the values for the other temperatures lay in between these. Thus the temperature optimum for vernalization shifts considerably depending on the length of exposure (10° for 15 days, 3 to 6° for 42 days), but ceases to exist if the exposure is long enough.

As in the rye embryos, cold given to the apex alone is sufficient to vernalize *Hyoscyamus* and many other biennials. The germinating seeds, however, are not vernalizable; this distinction between biennials and winter annuals is not always clear-cut, but in *Hyoscyamus* at least it is clear that seedlings are not sensitive to vernalization before 10 days of age, and not maximally sensitive until they are 30 days old (Sarkar, 1958). Work on the vernalization of *Hyoscyamus* has been reviewed by the original workers, Melchers and Lang (1948) and Lang (1952). Evidence for the existence of a translocatable product of vernalization has also been put forward and will be discussed in Chapter Five.

An exception to the observations that vernalization is perceived by the stem apex is found in *Streptocarpus wendlandii* (Oehlkers, 1956), in which the leaf appears to be the receptive region and neither embryo nor stem apex can be vernalized at all.

Several varieties of ornamental *Chrysanthemum* (*Chrysanthemum morifolium*) require vernalization. Here again the apex is the site of vernalization, and all the laterals subsequently derived from it over a long period of time show the vernalized condition (Schwabe, 1954). While most of the vernalizable plants studied require the treatment in order to respond as LDP, or are daylength-indifferent, vernalized *Chrysanthemum* is a quantitative SDP for both flower initiation and development. Three or four weeks at 4 to 5° C has an optimum vernalizing effect. Low temperature is effective even if given discontinuously, and a particular total number of hours given during each dark period is more effective than the same number of hours given only during light periods, at least under short-day conditions. *Chrysanthemum* is a perennial, and yet requires renewed vernalization each year (Schwabe, 1950), a situation probably characteristic of many such plants. This brings up the general topic of "devernalization," which has been observed in a number of plants.

DEVERNALIZATION

Vernalized seeds of Petkus winter rye can be devernalized simply by drying them and holding them in the dry condition for several weeks. However, only the effects of vernalization on the subsequent flowering response (to long days) are so reversed; the effects on vegetative growth are more complex. This is well illustrated by some data from Gregory and Purvis (1938a). Their unvernalized controls in this experiment produced about 4.7 tillers (lateral branches from the base) per plant, and a flowering "score" of 19. The "score" is an arbitrary scale adopted to indicate the intensity and earliness of flowering. Vernalized seed held dry for one day only (which has essentially no effect) gave a score of 51 and about 2.7 tillers per plant—vernalization typically decreases the number of tillers. Seed devernalized by being dry for 20 weeks, however, gave a score of 20 and about 13.7 tillers per plant; the promotion of flowering was completely reversed, but the number of tillers was much higher than in either vernalized or unvernalized plants. Thus devernalization here is not a simple reversal of vernalization but a conversion of its effects to a different physiological expression. Like vernalization itself, it is proportional, within limits, to the duration of exposure to the condition bringing it about.

Even spring Petkus rye, which may be regarded as already genetically vernalized, can be devernalized to some extent. The leaf number preceding flowering (in long days) is increased from an average of 6.8 to 8.3 by a three-week germination period under anaerobic conditions, and this effect is removed by a subsequent three-week vernalization treatment (Gregory and Purvis, 1938b).

The devernalization of vernalized biennial *Hyoscyamus* is brought about by relatively high temperatures. Vernalized plants may be kept under short-day conditions for at least several weeks at about 23° C and still retain their capacity to respond as LDP. Ten days at about 38° will completely remove this capacity, if started immediately after the vernalization treatment; if even a few days of moderate temperature intervene between vernalization and the high temperature, however, the vernalized condition becomes stabilized and can no longer be removed (Lang and Melchers, 1947). In general, studies of various plants indicate that the more complete the original vernalization and the greater the length of the treatment, the more difficult devernalization becomes. Revernalization after devernalization is also possible in certain plants.

As the only perennial studied in any detail, *Chrysanthemum* again appears unusual in that devernalization is not brought about by high temperatures alone, but requires several weeks of low light intensity (or darkness) as well as temperatures of 23° to 28° C. The mechanism of this effect is unknown. It is not due simply to starvation for carbohydrates since defoliation of the plants does not have the same effect, nor does sucrose feeding during treatment reduce devernalization (Schwabe, 1955b, 1957). Whether the devernalization that occurs in the natural yearly cycle is actually due to high temperatures and low light intensities (at the underground growing points) is still uncertain.

RELATIONS BETWEEN VERNALIZATION AND PHOTOPERIODISM

Many of the plants studied, and also work with the gibberellins (Chapter Six), may be used to support the idea of a close relationship between vernalization and long-day requirements, but the situation is probably more complex than this, varying greatly from plant to plant.

Petkus winter rye and biennial *Hyoscyamus niger* are "typical" vernalizable plants in which the cold treatment brings about quantitative or qualitative LDP responses. In other plants, vernalization can even substitute partially or completely for a long-day requirement. Vernalization of spinach seeds, for example, reduces the critical daylength for flowering from 14 to about 8 hours (Vlitos and Meudt, 1955), whereas cold treatments given to seedlings of certain strains of subterranean clover, *Trifolium subterraneum*, can completely remove any marked dependence on daylength (Evans, 1959).

Floral induction and development in several grasses depend upon both photoperiod and vernalization. Plants of orchard grass, *Dactylis glomerata*, studied by Gardner and Loomis (1953) require low temperatures and short days (less than 13 hours light) for floral induction, followed by higher temperatures and long days for optimum flower development. The short-day and vernalization requirements for induction can be satisfied separately but only in that order, not in the reverse. In a sense, then, *Dactylis glomerata* is one of the short-long-day plants (SLDP) mentioned in Chapter Two, except that a period of low temperature must occur between the two photoperiodic treatments or together with the first.

In some plants, short-day treatments can substitute partially or completely for vernalization, making them SLDP. Petkus winter rye itself shows a response of this kind, although the situation is complicated by the fact that both short days and continuous light favor flower initiation more than do long days in unvernalized plants (Gott *et al.,* 1955). A more clear-cut example of a vernalizable SLDP is *Campanula medium* (see Doorenbos and Wellensiek, 1959), which has a qualitative requirement for either low temperature or short days before it can respond to long days.

Although even in the above plants, vernalization generally has to be followed by exposure to long days, *Chrysanthemum* is not the only plant in which it promotes a response to short days. Junges (1958) found that short days following the vernalization of a strain of Kohlrabi, *Brassica oleracea* var. *gongyloides,* a biennial, promoted the subsequent flowering in long days and high temperatures. Such results make it unwise to regard vernalization requirements as necessarily linked to any other environmental response.

THE SEMANTICS OF VERNALIZATION: FURTHER EFFECTS OF TEMPERATURE ON FLOWERING

A restricted definition of vernalization was given earlier, but it is now time to acknowledge its fluidity. For one thing, the term is so often misapplied to the breaking of bud or embryo dormancy by low temperatures that it has become a mere jargon substitute for "cold treatment"; this is deplorable, but perhaps too late to mend. Even if one restricts its usage to effects on flowering, however, difficulties arise. It is clear enough how certain effects of near-freezing temperatures on biennials and perennials are similar to those on germinating winter annual seeds, and why the term vernalization may well be used for both. As long as one is dealing with an obviously inductive action on flowering of temperatures low enough to prevent growth, the phenomena seem relatively clear-cut. But when the same or very similar effects occur at temperatures high enough to allow rapid growth, or are not inductive, or interact with the conditions of light and darkness during exposure, are they still vernalization? This is not simply a matter of semantics; the point is that the influences of temperature on all aspects of development are so manifold that "typical" vernalization, as in rye or *Hyoscyamus,* probably is an extreme case of a very general situation. If so, then perhaps the erosion of the word vernalization is fortunate.

The plasticity of some vernalization requirements is illustrated by celery, *Apium graveolens* var. *dulce*. If the plants are kept at usual vernalizing temperatures (about 7° C) for a month, they will flower rapidly when transferred to cool (10–16°) or moderate (16–21°) but not warm (about 24°) conditions. The initial vernalization is not absolutely necessary for flowering, which will also take place eventually under constant cool conditions, or under the moderate conditions after two weeks under cool conditions. No temperature pretreatment of any kind will permit flower initiation under the warm conditions (Thompson, 1953). In short, vernalization is only weakly inductive and can take place at temperatures high enough to allow growth. The latter of course is true to a lesser extent even of *Hyoscyamus,* and one can still see in celery the occurrence of vernalization and devernalization in the *Hyoscyamus* sense, but the effective temperatures are considerably closer together.

The flowering response of stocks, *Matthiola incana,* as summarized by Kohl (1958), represents a situation in which it is uncertain whether the term vernalization can be applied or not. Neither germinating seeds nor seedlings can be induced by low temperatures, but maturing plants require at least three weeks at 10 to 16° C for flower initiation. If the temperature rises above 19° for as little as 6 hours per day, initiation is completely inhibited; the plants must remain at the favorably low temperatures until full differentiation of floral primordia has occurred. After this, however, they remain induced and produce new flower primordia even at the higher temperatures. This behavior can of course be regarded as vernalization with a very low degree of induction and a small difference between vernalizing and devernalizing temperatures, but speaking simply of optimum and maximum temperatures for flower initiation seems to be as accurate. Many plants probably respond in a similar fashion, with optima and maxima varying widely depending on the species.

Also relevant here is another temperature effect on plants, *thermoperiodism.* This term indicates the responses of plants to differing day and night temperatures—growth and development in most of those tested are favored by night temperatures markedly lower than those optimal during the light period (see Went, 1957). Work on this question will not be dealt with here, since relatively little of it directly concerns flower initiation. In addition, the interactions of temperature changes with high-intensity light periods of different lengths are extremely complex and have not been carefully analyzed. Many of the data do suggest, however, that "typical" vernalization, the effects of moderately low temperatures, the effects of varying day and night temperatures, and the interactions of temperature with photoperiod (Chapter Two) all intergrade.

Recall in this connection the observation of Schwabe (1955b, 1957) that discontinuous vernalizing cold treatments were more effective on *Chrysanthemum* when given during each night rather than in the day. This sounds very much like thermoperiodism. Note also that the tomato, *Lycopersicon esculentum,* in which major effects of temperature have been studied as thermoperiodism, is quantitatively vernalizable; exposure of the seedlings to temperatures near 10° C soon after cotyledon expansion significantly decreases the number of leaves formed before the first inflorescence and increases the number of flowers in that inflorescence (Wittwer and Teubner, 1956). Since one effect of low night temperatures is also to increase the number of flowers per inflorescence (Went, 1957, Chap. 6), vernalization in the tomato, as in *Chrysanthemum,* is perhaps not completely distinguishable from thermoperiodism.

A further expansion of the phenomena that need to be considered in connection with vernalization is suggested by some work of Guttridge (1958). By the definition previously given, vernalization results in the promotion of flowering. However, a cold treatment affects certain varieties of strawberry (*Fragaria*) in the opposite fashion, inductively bringing about a condition in which flower initiation is delayed and runner production promoted when the plants are subsequently transferred to conditions that would otherwise make for continued flowering and low vegetative growth. This effect is certainly formally similar to vernalization, though inverse in result.

TEMPERATURE AND FLOWERING IN BULB PLANTS

Among the most detailed studies yet done on temperature and flowering are those of Blaauw, Hartsema, Luyten, and their collaborators in the Netherlands, particularly in the period 1920–1935, on the initiation and development of flowers in bulb plants. This work is largely recorded in Dutch but has been reviewed by Went (1948), from whom this account is taken. The basic procedure was to store bulbs at different temperatures for different lengths of time and determine, by anatomical studies, the optimum temperature for the various developmental events taking place within them.

After the current year's foliage has died, the next year's apical meristem within the tulip (*Tulipa*) bulb already has several leaf primordia. Flower initiation, including differentiation of all the flower parts, then takes about three weeks at 20° C, the optimal temperature for this process. If further flower development is to take place (still entirely within the bulb), the temperature must now drop and remain at about 9° C for 13 to 14 weeks. After this low-temperature period the optimal temperatures for leaf and stalk elongation are successively higher, reaching 20° and above for complete anthesis. This increase in optimal temperature for the final stages of flowering is more or less gradual, but it appears to be characteristic of tulip and certain other plants that flower initiation, favored by relatively high temperatures, must be followed quite abruptly by low temperatures for the best subsequent development. In the hyacinth (*Hyacinthus*) bulb, on the other hand, the changes in temperature optima are not as abrupt as in the tulip, though they are similar, and all the values lie somewhat higher.

Such studies have since been conducted, in the Netherlands and elsewhere, on many plants having bulbs, rhizomes, or other fleshy organs that can be stored for a considerable part of the year. The detailed results of course differ from plant to plant, but are usually of great practical value since they make it possible to control development or arrest it at desired stages to suit almost any shipping and planting schedule. Tulips and hyacinths, for example, can be held completely dormant without injury for weeks by storage at 35° C. As soon as further development is required, the temperature can again be lowered to the optimal level for the stage previously attained. Recent references to this sort of work can be found in journals and textbooks on horticulture.

It needs to be stressed that this sort of temperature response is not characteristic of all bulb plants, but merely of those adapted to temperate climates with a well-defined winter. The tropical bulb

Hippeastrum, for example, also studied by Blaauw (see Went, 1948), has no such requirement for a long period of low temperature, and flowers several times a year at high or moderate temperatures. The similarity between the cold requirement in a plant such as the tulip and typical vernalization should also be noted. Here of course the effect is on flower development, not induction or initiation, but the conditions involved and the final results are the same, although the underlying physiological conditions are unknown in any case.

Unlike light or certain chemical factors, temperature cannot be given or withheld but only changed, and it affects essentially all biochemical processes. This makes it at once the most important single factor in development and the most difficult to study in any delimited way. Hence it is not surprising that terms such as vernalization are almost meaningless except to indicate a particular kind of manipulation, and may not designate any single specific physiological process. The brevity of this discussion relative to those on other factors affecting flowering should be taken to reflect not a lesser importance of its problems, but only how little is known about them in any fundamental sense. See Went (1953, 1957) for a much more thorough treatment of the effects of temperature on all aspects of plant growth; a review by Chouard (1960) emphasizes the complexity of vernalization and related low-temperature effects.

chapter five Floral Hormones
and the Induced State

Even before the effects of light and temperature—the major
natural environmental influences on flowering—were known, the
question of what internal changes lead to flowering was of obvious
importance; photoperiodism and, to a lesser extent, vernalization
made experimental approaches to it more feasible. The next three
chapters are largely concerned with this question in one way or
another; the present will examine the nature and origin of substances controlling flowering and transmissible from one part of a
plant to another or from plant to plant by grafting.

DEFINITIONS AND BACKGROUND: AUXINS AS PLANT HORMONES

Hormones can be defined as substances produced in one part
of an organism and acting in another, and active in very low concentrations. Action at a distance from the site of production is the
most crucial characteristic of a hormone; activity in low concentrations simply serves to distinguish it from substances furnishing
energy or structural materials and used in large quantities. Sugars,
for example, are produced in aerial parts of the plant and used
in the roots (as well as elsewhere) but cannot be considered hormones.

The idea that the formation of flowers, and of other organs as well, is controlled by hormones specific for each type of organ—"organ-forming substances"—was favored in the nineteenth century by Julius Sachs, the so-called "father of plant physiology." Evidence at the time was almost nonexistent; more recent evidence, at least for flowering hormones, will be considered below. First, however, it is useful to describe briefly a different and better known class of plant hormones, the auxins. Research on these substances, starting in the 1920's, has had a strong influence on the less successful investigations on possible flowering hormones; in addition, auxins may play at least a minor role in the control of flowering.

If the tip of a growing shoot is removed, the elongation of the remaining stump generally ceases rapidly. If the tip is replaced, the stump may resume and continue elongating for some time, although not necessarily as fast as in the intact plant. This effect of the tip may even occur if it is separated from the stump by a thin layer of agar or gelatin. In such cases, elongation can be brought about simply by placing on the stump a piece of gelatin or agar on which the cut surface of the tip, or several similar tips, have rested for some time. Such results indicate that a substance or substances that can move out of the tip and into or through gelatin are required for the continued elongation of the tissue below. Such substances are termed auxins. It is now known that low concentrations of many substances, both natural and synthetic, can promote the elongation of shoot tissue deprived of its natural auxin sources. Most of them are relatively simple organic compounds, such as indole-3-acetic acid; those occurring naturally are clearly plant hormones since they are produced in shoot tips (or other young, actively growing regions) and affect tissues elsewhere. The action of auxins is not confined to causing the elongation of shoot cells, however; depending on the concentration, they may either promote or inhibit many plant processes, including root initiation, leaf abscission, and cell division. Space forbids further discussion of auxins as such, but they will figure in a number of the topics to be considered. For additional information on the general topic of auxin physiology, which has a voluminous literature, see Audus (1959), Leopold (1955), or the recent volume, *Plant Growth Regulation* (1961).

PRELIMINARY EVIDENCE FOR THE EXISTENCE
OF FLOWERING HORMONES

The clearest early investigations indicating the existence of floral hormones were by Chailakhyan in Russia. One of his major experiments (1936a) showed that if the upper portion of the SDP *Chrysanthemum indicum* were defoliated, it would initiate flowers if the lower (leafy) portion received short days, even if the defoliated part were kept on long days. With the conditions reversed —if the upper defoliated part were kept on short days and the lower leaves on long days—no flowering occurred. He interpreted these results as indicating that under the proper photoperiodic conditions the leaves could form a hormone that moved to the apex and brought about flowering. From subsequent work he concluded also that this hormone, which he named "florigen" (flower-maker), could move either up or down the stem and could be transferred from one plant to another through grafts (Chailakhyan, 1936b, 1936c, 1937).

Several investigators at first obtained data suggesting that florigen, like the auxins, could pass through a nonliving connection, but these proved to be illusory. Moshkov (1939), for example, soon reported his inability to repeat his own earlier experiment in which the *Chrysanthemum* floral stimulus had apparently passed through a thin film of water, and he concluded that such movement could take place only through living tissue. A similar encouraging but false start was made by Hamner and Bonner (1938). They showed that a photoperiodically induced *Xanthium* plant grafted to a noninduced plant could bring about flowering in the latter. They further observed that interposition of a piece of fine lens paper between the stock and scion would still permit this effect. This suggested that florigen could move from the induced plant (the donor) to the noninduced plant (the receptor) without direct tissue contact. When this work was repeated by Withrow and Withrow (1943), using various kinds of membranes including lens paper between the cut surfaces of donor and receptor, it appeared that the original interpretation was mistaken. Anatomical studies showed that tissue union could occur by the growth of cells through the lens paper; the transmission of florigen took place only when there was such union, and all membranes that would prevent actual "taking" of the graft also prevented transmission.

Chailakhyan (1937) had already concluded from experiments with *Perilla* and *Chrysanthemum,* and the Withrows (1943) confirmed with *Xanthium,* that florigen movement occurred only through the "bark"—the phloem and cortical tissue. If this was removed in ringing or girdling experiments, no movement of the floral stimulus across the girdle was observed, although water continued to pass through the xylem (wood) and the shoots remained healthy. Presumably the major route of transport is the phloem itself, in which most organic substances are transported; but we will return to this question later.

Questions obvious from the start of this kind of research are whether the florigen of one kind of plant is effective on another and, more particularly, whether that of an SDP will act on an LDP and vice versa. Auxins are not species-specific, but such questions are more difficult to answer with respect to flowering hormones, transmissible from plant to plant only by grafting. Successful grafts are generally possible only between closely related plants so that no completely general answer can be given. Within these limitations, however, the floral stimulus produced by one species is often effective on other, closely related species.

Maryland Mammoth tobacco and annual *Hyoscyamus niger* are members of the same family (Solanaceae) and can be successfully grafted. In such a graft partnership, the LDP *Hyoscyamus* will flower under short-day conditions if the SDP tobacco is also kept under short days, but not if the tobacco is exposed to long days. That is, under short days the tobacco is itself induced and serves as the donor of stimulus of florigen to *Hyoscyamus*. Conversely, the tobacco can be made to flower under long-day conditions if the *Hyoscyamus* is induced by also being kept under long days, but not if the *Hyoscyamus* receives short days. Here *Hyoscyamus* becomes the donor and Maryland Mammoth the receptor (Lang and Melchers, 1947; see Lang, 1952). The simplest conclusion is of course that the florigens produced by *Hyoscyamus* in long days and by Maryland Mammoth tobacco in short days are physiologically equivalent if not identical.

There are many similar experiments in the literature. The SDP *Xanthium,* for example, can be made to flower on long days when grafted to any of several LDP members of its family, the composites, such as species of *Erigeron* or *Rudbeckia* (Okuda, 1953). Using members of the family Crassulaceae, Zeevaart (1958) found that the LDP *Sedum ellacombianum* or *Sedum spectabile*

A   **B**

Fig. 5-1. Transfer of flowering stimulus between LDP and SDP by grafting, showing role of leaves. (*A*) Induction of flowering in an LDP (*Sedum spectabile*) in short days by grafting onto an SDP (*Kalanchoë blossfeldiana*). In the graft to the right, the *Kalanchoë* (below) was kept defoliated. Photograph made 96 days after grafting. (*B*) Induction of flowering in an SDP (*Kalanchoë*) in long days by grafting onto an LDP (*Sedum*)—the reciprocal of the experiment in (*A*). Again, in the graft to the right, the *Sedum* was kept defoliated. Photograph made 130 days after grafting. (Photographs from Zeevaart [1958], courtesy of Dr. J. A. D. Zeevaart, Agricultural Institute, Wageningen.)

could flower under short days when grafted onto the SDP *Kalanchoë blossfeldiana,* whereas the latter would flower under long days when grafted to the *Sedums* (see Fig. 5-1). Such effects can be turned to practical use. Many varieties of the cultivated sweet potato, *Ipomoea batatas,* flower irregularly if at all, no matter what the environmental conditions, which is a distinct hindrance to breeding programs. This recalcitrance can be overcome by grafting shoots to any of several free-flowering (SDP) genera of the same family (Convolvulaceae—morning glories) and then inducing the latter (Lam *et al.,* 1959).

The occurrence of transmissible flowering stimuli is not confined to photoperiodic plants. This is of course implicit in the fact, noted earlier, that many plants are only quantitatively photoperiodic, or are photoperiodic only under certain conditions, whereas some are completely daylength-indifferent; the processes leading to flowering may or may not be under photoperiodic control and still have the same end result. Lang (1952) has reviewed work in which daylength-indifferent plants can serve as donors of a flowering stimulus to closely related LDP or SDP.

Not all results on the transmission of flowering stimuli have been straightforward, and before proceeding further it is well to keep the fundamental difficulty in mind. Auxins can be obtained from plants either by diffusion from cut tissues, as previously described, or by extraction. They can then be reapplied and will cause growth in responsive tissue. This makes possible not only the identification and quantitative assay of naturally occurring auxins but also the study of the biochemistry of their origin and function. Not so for the hypothetical florigen—which remains hypothetical for the very reason that, with one possible exception, no work to date has successfully isolated it from the living plant; attempts to do so will be discussed in the following chapter. Thus it has not been possible to study flowering hormones chemically, and all the evidence is necessarily circumstantial. Hence the use in this chapter of all sorts of terms—florigen, floral hormones, flowering stimuli, and so on—to avoid implying a precision that does not exist. We must now pay closer attention to the experimental systems involved in such work—the plants themselves—following which we can return more critically to the question of whether floral hormones actually exist.

TRANSLOCATION OF FLOWERING HORMONES

The conclusion that florigen moves only through living tissues is based on observations besides those already presented. Borthwick, Parker, and Heinze (1941) showed that a soybean plant defoliated to only a single leaf could flower in short days, but not if the petiole was chilled to 3° C. This was true even if another leaf was left on the plant, below the first, and exposed to long days without any other treatment. Hence the inhibition of flowering was not due simply to lack of carbohydrate transport through the chilled petiole, since carbohydrates were still supplied by the long-day leaf, but to the inhibition of the transport of the stimulus specifically from the short-day leaf. These and similar results indicate that transport is the result of cellular activity. Further circumstantial evidence implicates the phloem in florigen transport by indicating that the latter is associated with the movement of carbohydrates in the plant. This evidence is not unequivocal, and is based largely on experiments dealing with the effects of noninduced leaves on the flowering response.

Note that in Chailakhyan's experiment with *Chrysanthemum*, discussed earlier, the upper portion of the plant was defoliated in order to demonstrate the movement of a flowering stimulus from the lower leaves on short days. Many observations, including those of Chailakhyan, indicate that in some plants translocation can only be demonstrated in this manner. A technique often used to study this sort of question involves the use of two-branched plants, produced by removing the apical portion of seedlings and allowing two approximately equal lateral branches to develop. One branch can then be exposed to inductive conditions, making it the donor of flowering stimulus, and the other, on noninductive conditions, is used as the receptor. When Biloxi soybeans are used in this way, the receptor (long-day) branches flower only if they are defoliated but not if the leaves are left in place, even though the donor branch flowers well whether or not the receptor has leaves (Borthwick and Parker, 1938b). Similar results have been obtained in other plants but are by no means universal. In the SDP *Amaranthus caudatus*, defoliation of the receptor (long-day) branches greatly inhibits, rather than promotes, their flowering, which is otherwise almost as rapid as that of the donor branch itself (Fuller, 1949).

Noninduced leaves can be kept in total darkness, rather than removed, in order to avoid their inhibiting transmission. This observation was actually first made by Garner and Allard in 1925; the only reason they are not generally credited with the discovery of the translocatable effects of photoperiodism is that they themselves stressed the localization of such effects in *Cosmos*, the SDP they chose for work on this question. In this as in many other plants, flowering in normal, intact individuals is confined to the area exposed to induction. A portion of the plant kept in total darkness, however, will exhibit a flowering response, provided an adjacent portion is kept on inducing (short-day) conditions. An elegant experiment by Stout (1945) illustrates the same situation for an LDP, the sugar beet (*Beta vulgaris*). Plants with three shoots were made by root grafts. If one of these shoots was exposed to long days, it flowered and also brought about flowering in a second shoot kept in darkness. The third shoot, however, maintained on short days, remained vegetative.

As suggested earlier, most experiments of this kind can be interpreted as indicating that florigen moves in the prevailing direction of carbohydrate movement. In this view, darkening or removing leaves from a noninduced part of the plant results in a lower carbohydrate production in that part, so that carbohydrate (and florigen) movement in its direction is increased. There are alternative explanations, however, as will become evident later. In some cases, darkened leaves may inhibit translocation; this has been interpreted as a "diversion" of the movement into such leaves (see Lang, 1952).

Interesting evidence on the translocation of floral hormones and the effects of noninduced leaves comes from work on the SDP *Kalanchoë blossfeldiana* reported by Harder (1948). With a minimal short-day treatment, development of the complex, branching inflorescence is slow and "vegetative"; that is, the flowers are small or abortive and the bracts among them overdeveloped and leaflike. If only a single leaf receives short-day treatment, inflorescence development may be normal, provided the treatment continues long enough; but commonly it is notably asymmetrical, being more normal on the side directly above the induced leaf and vegetative on the side away from it (see Fig. 5-2). Examination of the vascular system shows that this is consistent with the idea that florigen simply moves in the phloem; the lateral connections in *Kalanchoë* are relatively minor, so that little lateral movement of the effect would be expected.

Experiments on the effects of noninduced leaves in *Kalanchoë* depend on its decussate leaf arrangement; that is, each pair of opposite leaves is at right angles to the pair above or below it. Thus looking down on the plant one sees four ranks of leaves at right angles to each other. If all but two leaves (of different pairs) are removed from the plant, and the lower is given short days and the upper long days, several different results can be obtained. If the long-day leaf is in the same rank with (directly above) the long-day leaf, flowering is prevented. If the long-day leaf is in the rank opposite that of the short-day leaf, flowering is the same as if

Fig. 5-2. Localization of flowering stimulus in *Kalanchoë*. A single leaf situated on the left-hand side was repeatedly exposed to short days whereas the rest of the plant received long days. (Photograph from Harder [1948], by permission of the company of Biologists, Ltd., and courtesy of Dr. R. Harder, University of Göttingen.)

the long-day leaf were absent. Finally, if the long-day leaf is in either of the two ranks at right angles to that of the short-day leaf, some inhibition of flowering is evident. In this sort of experiment, the transport of florigen is evidently upward from leaf to growing point, but appropriately trimmed plants can be used for similar studies on the transport downward from a short-day leaf to an axillary shoot. Here again, a long-day leaf between the short-day leaf and the shoot inhibits most effectively if it is in the same rank, and least effectively if it is in the rank opposite. In short, whether movement is up or down, the inhibition only occurs if the non-induced leaf lies effectively between the induced leaf and the growing point in question. This is apparently true for many plants besides *Kalanchoë* and is again consistent with the postulated movement of florigen with the carbohydrate stream. In addition, however, it is also consistent with the idea that the flowering hormone might be taken up by the noninduced tissue and destroyed by it.

The latter interpretation is also suggested by analogous experiments in which parts of a single leaf are subjected to long-day or short-day treatments. If the basal part of the leaf is given short days and the apical long days, flowering occurs, but if the situation is reversed, the flowering is weak or absent. This is not due to the inability of the apical portion to respond to short days and lead to flowering, since it does so if the entire basal part is trimmed off as long as the vascular connection to the stem is left intact. Here again, noninduced tissue evidently inhibits flowering when it is situated between induced tissue and the growing point, and possibly does so by destroying the floral stimulus. Earlier experiments by Chailakhyan with *Perilla* leaves also lead to the same conclusion (see Naylor, 1953).

The most thorough recent studies of the interactions of various parts of the plant on the effectiveness of localized inducing treatments are those of Lincoln, Raven, and Hamner (1956, 1958), using *Xanthium*. The first paper bears most directly on translocation. With two-branched plants, the intensity of flowering in the receptor branch (long days) is inversely proportional to the amount of mature tissue left on it. If, however, a carbohydrate deficiency is produced in the receptor by heavy shade, the inhibition by the long-day leaves is greatly reduced. Conversely, shading the donor (short-day) branch, which would produce a carbohydrate deficit in it, reduces flowering in the receptor. So also does removing the receptor's young leaves, which are responsible for a great portion of its carbohydrate uptake. Although these results are consistent with the carbohydrate-flow hypothesis, several others suggest a more complex situation. The inhibiting effect of mature leaves on the receptor is not simply proportional to the amount of light they receive but depends on its timing; that is, the effect is photoperiodic. For example, the inhibition caused by leaves given 12 hours light-12 hours dark cycles is much greater if each night is interrupted by three evenly spaced 10-minute light-breaks than if interrupted only once, in the middle, by a 30-minute light-break. If only carbohydrate production were involved in the inhibition, such results would not be expected.

In certain plants, such as the SDP *Piqueria trinervia* (stevia), the effect of inductive treatment remains relatively localized no matter what manipulations are performed (Zimmerman and Kjennerud, 1950). Thus the only summary statement that can be made about the movement or apparent movement of flowering hormones is that it takes place in living tissue, probably through the phloem; that it can be either acropetal (base to apex) or basipetal; that it may be localized or systemic depending on the plant, the structure of its vascular system, and the condition of noninduced portions. There is evidence that noninduced leaves act in an inhibitory fashion primarily but not exclusively by affecting the predominant direction of carbohydrate movement, with which the florigen may be carried.

TRANSLOCATION RATE

There are very few studies on the rate of movement of floral stimuli, again because of the difficulty that only the final response, not the postulated hormone, can be measured. Early work by Chailakhyan suggested values of about 2 cm in 24 hours in *Perilla,* but it is doubtful whether conditions were optimal (see Lang, 1952). Some ingenious experiments by Imamura and Takimoto (1955b) provide the best data so far available.

Plants of the SDP *Pharbitis nil* (Japanese morning glory) can be reduced to a stem with a single leaf, and then decapitated so that the bud in the axil of the leaf will start to grow. The position of the first flower on the axillary shoot will then depend on the time between the start of growth (decapitation) and the start of a single 16-hour inductive dark period given to the leaf. In one experiment, for example, if the dark period was started immediately after decapitation, the average position of the first flower on the axillary shoot was at node 2.8 (that is, node 2 in some plants, node 3 in most). If 24 hours elapsed between decapitation and the dark period, the average position was node 3.5, and so on. Such differences are developmental expressions of the amount of time during which the axillary bud (shoot) was growing before the flowering stimulus reached it. Parallel experiments can be done at the same time with plants in which the distance between the single leaf and the receptor bud is greater—for example, by having the latter not in the axil of the leaf but on the opposite branch of an otherwise debudded two-branched plant. The rate of stimulus translocation can then be calculated by the difference in the first-flowering-node values of the shoots in the plants with the receptor buds close and the receptor buds far from the induced leaf. An example from one experiment may make this clear. In the "close" series, in which the average distance from leaf to bud (mainly through petiole tissue) was 90 mm, the mean first flowering node was 3.4 if the dark treatment was given 24 hours after decapitation, 4.5 with it given 48 hours after, and 5.3 with it given 72 hours after. In the "far" series, the distance between leaf and bud was about 235 mm, through both branch and petiole tissue. Here, inductive treatment started immediately after decapitation gave a first-flowering-node average of 4.6. By interpolation from the preceding figures, it is as if the inductive treatment for the "close" series had been delayed some 55 hours. Since the difference between "far" and "close" is about 145 mm, this difference of 55 hours represents the movement of the stimulus at 145/55, or about 2.6 mm per hour.

Such experiments of course give an average value for the transport through a petiole, then both down and up a branch; other experiments suggested that upward transport may be faster than downward. Also, the transport rate in plants so mutilated may well differ from that in intact plants. In any case, all experiments with *Pharbitis* gave values of the order of 3 mm per hour. This represents a considerably slower movement than that observed for carbohydrates in phloem tissue (often exceeding 200 mm per hour), but rates of virus transport in the phloem sometimes fall in this low range (see Esau *et al.*, 1957).

FLOWER PROMOTION OR FLOWER INHIBITION? THE SPECIFICITY OF FLOWERING STIMULI

The florigen hypothesis in its simplest form postulates a single substance, common at least to many plants, uniquely responsible for flower initiation. Much of the evidence so far presented is consistent with this hypothesis, but some investigators, on the contrary, have concluded that flowering is controlled by an inhibitory substance or substances that prevent initiation until they are removed by the proper conditions.

It may be surprising that most of the very evidence presented in the preceding section for movement of a florigen can be reinterpreted as indicating simply deinhibition (see von Denffer, 1950). Under this interpretation, noninduced leaves constantly produce a flowering inhibitor that moves to the growing point along with the products of photosynthesis; induced leaves no longer produce this inhibitor. Hence the removal or darkening of noninduced leaves often promotes flowering not, as under the florigen hypothesis, by preventing interference with the carbohydrate stream in which the florigen moves, but by reducing still further the sources of the inhibitor; flowering thus occurs simply as a result of sufficient quantities of inhibitor-free assimilates. It has been suggested, on the basis of work to be discussed later, that the inhibitor in question might be an auxin, and the general form of this hypothesis fits some of the experimental data well enough. At least, it often fits no worse than the other hypothesis, as a brief reconsideration will show.

Stout's (1945) work with "three-headed" beet plants indicated that the presence of a shoot on short-day conditions did not inhibit the response of a darkened receptor shoot to the long-day donor shoot; thus if the noninduced (short-day) shoot produces an inhibitor, it is not detectable. This does not help the inhibitor hypothesis. On the other hand, the further result that even 4 hours of light per day (compared with 17 hours for the donor) prevents a shoot from being an effective receptor also does not help the simple florigen-movement-with-carbohydrates hypothesis, since it is unlikely that the predominant direction of carbohydrate movement would be reversed under these conditions. Another ambiguous situation is of course that the inhibitory effect of noninduced *Xanthium* leaves appears to be a photoperiodic phenomenon in its own right, not simply a matter of affecting carbohydrate (and florigen) flow.

The florigen hypothesis can be saved from many difficulties, including these, by the suggestion that noninduced leaves act not by producing an inhibitor but by destroying florigen. On balance, the simple inhibitor hypothesis is probably less satisfactory; the strongest argument against it is the effectiveness of small amounts of induced leaf tissue, of which there are many examples in the literature. *Xanthium* is striking in this regard. Several double-branched plants grafted together in series can all be brought to flower by short-day treatment of a single leaf on one of them (see Naylor, 1953). Khudairi and Hamner (1954a) found that a total leaf area of less than one square centimeter was enough to bring about flowering from a single 16-hour dark period. *Xanthium* may be more extreme in this regard than most species, but the idea that induced leaves simply supply an inhibitor-free stream of assimilates is hard to reconcile with such results. However, some form of inhibitor hypothesis is still favored by certain investigations, of which a few should be considered.

In annual *Hyoscyamus* (LDP), removal of all the leaves brings about flower formation, which then takes place at the same rate irrespective of light or dark conditions. Presumably, then, the effect of long days on an intact plant is to prevent an inhibition of flowering exerted by the leaves under short-day conditions. Since clearly in the defoliated plant the floral stimulus is present or can be formed in the stem or roots, leaves on short days apparently not only fail to produce it themselves, but also destroy it, or inhibit its production, or produce an inhibitor of flowering. The latter hypothesis can be avoided either by adopting the first or by suggesting a mechanism for the second—for example, that the short-day leaves remove some substance that could otherwise act as a precursor for production of the stimulus. So far, there is no clear evidence in any direction (see Lang, 1952). Whatever the explanation, such effects may be responsible for some of the ambiguous results obtained from grafting experiments, as in the following example taken from Zeevaart (1958).

Defoliated scions of the LDP *Nicotiana sylvestris* grafted on stocks of the SDP Maryland Mammoth will flower on short days, suggesting florigen transfer from the induced stock. However, such scions also flower on long days, noninductive for Maryland Mammoth, although similarly defoliated but ungrafted *Nicotiana sylvestris* fails to flower on long days. Does Maryland Mammoth then produce florigen under, for it, noninductive conditions? The explanation may be that defoliated *Nicotiana sylvestris*, like *Hyoscyamus*, has the capacity to flower if sufficient assimilates are present. In *Hyoscyamus* these come from the large storage root, whereas in the *Nicotiana sylvestris* experiment they are supplied by Maryland Mammoth whether on long or short days.

Flower initiation in strawberries, *Fragaria*, requires short days, at least under certain conditions. Hartmann (1947) showed that daughter plants would initiate flowers in long days if the adult plant, to which they were still connected by runners, was exposed to short days; he interpreted these results in the conventional "florigen" manner. Guttridge (1959) has since performed experiments suggesting the opposite—that flowering occurs when the level of a flowering inhibitor, which also promotes vegetative growth, is sufficiently reduced. This postulated substance would be produced in long but not in short days, and might even be destroyed in the latter. The evidence is analogous to that on the translocation of flowering hormones.

Plants kept on long photoperiods (using light-breaks) promote vegetative growth and inhibit flowering in runner-attached plants under short photoperiods. This is favored by earlier daily illumination of the plants on long days, although earlier illumination itself, without light-breaks to create an effective long photoperiod, has no effect. These results of course again suggest translocation of the substance in question—this time the flower-inhibiting, growth-promoting substance—in the predominant direction of carbohydrate movement. Experiments with radioactive phosphorus as a tracer confirmed the postulated direction of assimilate movement. Guttridge's results are thus more consistent with the "simple inhibitor" hypothesis than with "florigen"; here the "donor" is vegetative, the "receptor" potentially flowering.

The earliness of flowering in certain pea varieties—by which is meant whether the first flower appears at a lower or higher node —can be influenced in several ways other than (in some varieties) photoperiod or cold treatment. These include removing the cotyledons, making cuttings from the young seedlings, grafting of early onto late varieties or vice versa, or even grafting stock and scion of the same variety. The situation is complicated by the fact that certain treatments, which can be broadly described as inhibitory, may inhibit vegetative growth more than flowering so that the latter actually occurs at an earlier node, though no sooner in time. Haupt (1958) has concluded on the basis of his own experiments and those of others that transmissible flower-promoting and flower-inhibiting substances both play a part in these effects, but their nature is unknown.

Resende (1959) also supports the concept that flowering generally depends on a change in a complex balance rather than on either simple flower-promoting or flower-inhibiting substances, since his experiments with the Crassulaceae (*Bryophyllum, Kalanchoë, Bryokalanchoë* species) have indicated all degrees of transfer of the "floral state" or "vegetative state" from one plant to another by grafting. Further discussion on the merits of various hypotheses will be deferred until the concluding section of the chapter.

VERNALIN AND METAPLASIN

In addition to florigen and flowering inhibitors, the participation of other transmissible substances in flowering or processes related to it has been suggested. With regard to vernalization, Melchers (see Melchers and Lang, 1948; Lang, 1952) has assumed the existence of a substance called "vernalin" on the basis of experiments with biennial *Hyoscyamus*. If two of these *Hyoscyamus*, one previously vernalized and one unvernalized, are grafted together, both will flower in response to long days, although an unvernalized plant alone will not. This might indeed be due to transfer of vernalin from the vernalized to the unvernalized plant, but it can be equally interpreted as a movement of floral stimulus from the vernalized, long-day treated plant to the other that, unvernalized, cannot respond to long days. The "vernalin" interpretation is based on the additional observation that unvernalized biennial *Hyoscyamus* grafted to Maryland Mammoth tobacco will flower in long days, in which the tobacco itself is not induced. The tobacco is visualized as a donor of vernalin—produced without vernalization in a non-cold-requiring plant—enabling the unvernalized biennial to respond to long days. In this view, vernalin is either a direct biochemical precursor of florigen or makes its synthesis possible.

The difficulties of interpreting grafting experiments with tobacco (*Nicotiana*) species, some of which were mentioned earlier, make this evidence less than completely convincing. To the writer's knowledge, there has never been any clear demonstration of the transmission, by grafting or otherwise, of a stimulus resulting from vernalization alone rather than vernalization followed by long days; such a demonstration would be necessary to establish the existence of vernalin.

In the course of work on *Kalanchoë*, Harder (1948) concluded that short-day treatment caused the production not only of flowering hormones but also of "metaplasin," a substance responsible for the large and easily measured changes in vegetative habit (particularly leaf succulence) accompanying flowering. Studies on its transport, analogous to those on the floral hormones in *Kalanchoë*, did not permit any separation of one from the other. The entire evidence for the existence of metaplasin as a separate entity is this: subjecting the upper portion of a plant on short days to a prolonged chloroform treatment that will strongly inhibit flowering has no influence on the vegetative effects of the photoperiod. This is hardly unequivocal proof that short days result in the production of two different substances, one specific for flowering and one for the vegetative changes. It is equally reasonable to assume that the processes leading to flowering are in some way different and more sensitive to this inhibition than those controlling vegetative growth, but it does not follow that the initiating conditions or substance brought about by photoperiodic treatment is necessarily multiple.

If the conclusion at present must be that vernalin and metaplasin may be myths, they nevertheless serve a purpose here. They remind us, to whom these particular errors may seem obvious, that the difficulties of analyzing the responses of complex organisms, coupled with the desire to achieve simple interpretations, may lead even some foremost investigators astray.

PERMANENCE AND LOCATION OF THE INDUCED STATE

As indicated in the preceding chapters, the effect of a particular treatment, temperature or photoperiodic, may persist and be expressed in flowering response later, even though no anatomical changes are evident when the treatment is stopped. Induction, as this aftereffect is called, is widespread though not universal, and differs considerably in both permanence and location within the plant. Confining this discussion first to the photoperiodically induced state, we find that it is transient in certain plants—that is, they may require almost continuous exposure to the appropriate photoperiod in order to flower—and remarkably long-lived in others (see, for example, Doorenbos and Wellensiek, 1959; Chouard, 1957). Probably most plants are at neither extreme but, like Biloxi soybean, revert to vegetative growth after flowering over a period proportional to the previous photoperiodic treatment (Borthwick and Parker, 1938a; Hamner, 1940). For obvious reasons, however, the induced state has been studied chiefly in a few plants in which it is relatively permanent, notably in two SDP, *Xanthium* and *Perilla*.

The induced state in *Xanthium* is both persistent and transmissible from plant to plant. The transfer of a florigen from a single leaf on short days through several grafted plants has already been mentioned, but it is possible to separate the final receptor from the short-day donor in time as well. If a plant induced by short days is grafted to a receptor plant in long days, the latter will flower. If the first graft is broken and the first receptor then grafted to another vegetative plant, that plant will also flower on long days, and so on (see Bonner, 1959a). Thus the induced state, by which is meant here the capacity to continue producing florigen, appears to be transferable from plant to plant along with the florigen itself; this might be called "indirect" induction, in contrast to direct induction by short days.

If all the actively growing buds of a single-leaved *Xanthium* plant are removed before and for a few days after a single short-day cycle, the plant remains vegetative. A given leaf can produce the flowering stimulus, but not over a long period of time; the young leaves and buds can apparently be indirectly induced by older leaves, however, and can themselves either store or continue to produce the stimulus in quantity. The experiments indicating this interaction are too complex to describe here (Salisbury, 1955; Lincoln, Raven, and Hamner, 1958), but suggest that in *Xanthium* the induced state is not permanently localized but depends on the renewed indirect induction of the younger portions of the plant.

The situation obtaining in *Perilla,* as reported by both Lona (1959) and Zeevaart (1958), is quite different. A photoperiodically induced leaf continues to produce florigen throughout its life. It can be grafted onto a plant on long days, bringing it to flower, then removed and grafted onto another plant, with the same result; this can be repeated as long as the leaf remains healthy, which may be for several months (see Fig. 5-3). There is no evidence that any other part of the plant has a role in the maintenance of the induced state; detached leaves are easily induced by the appropriate photoperiod, as can be demonstrated by subsequently grafting them onto plants on long days. Experiments of this kind are rarely successful with *Xanthium*. The clearest difference between *Perilla* and *Xanthium* lies in the lack of any indirect induction in the former. When *Perilla* in long days is brought to flower by grafting an induced leaf to it, the leaves it subsequently produces remain noninduced, incapable of causing flowering in another plant on long days.

On the basis of these observations, the relationship between florigen and the induced state in *Perilla* and *Xanthium* appears to differ considerably. In the former, the induced state is localized in the leaf, produced only by photoperiodic treatment and obviously separable from the transmitted florigen. In *Xanthium*, indirect induction of the developing leaves goes on continually, either as a result of the transmission of florigen itself—in which case the production of floral stimulus in *Xanthium* is autocatalytic—or brought about by a second unknown substance moving with it. Without further evidence, the first possibility clearly requires the fewest assumptions, although it raises problems which will be considered later.

As the induced states in *Xanthium* and *Perilla* are maintained in different ways, their permanence also differs. Implicit in much of the *Xanthium* literature is the idea that, once induced, a plant remains induced throughout its lifetime. In a sense this is not true, since Lam and Leopold (1960) showed that reversion can be brought about by constantly removing the flowering shoots and forcing new ones to grow out, until finally vegetative shoots appear. Several interpretations of these results have been suggested, none preferable to others on the basis of available evidence; but it is nevertheless clear that without such drastic treatment, *Xanthium* seldom or never reverts even after induction by a single short-day cycle. The *Perilla* plant, unlike *Xanthium*, reverts easily to the vegetative state under long days, since the induced older leaves die and there is no indirect induction to reinduce the younger. It is thus some-

A

B

Fig. 5-3. Experiments with grafting of single leaves in *Perilla*. (*A*) Technique. *Left*, donor leaf in polyethylene bag. *Right*, bag removed; in this case the leaf has been trimmed to give a standard surface area. (*B*) Induction of flowering in long days by a grafted leaf previously exposed to 36 short days. Photograph made 41 days after grafting. (Photographs from Zeevaart [1958], courtesy of Dr. J. A. D. Zeevaart, Agricultural Institute, Wageningen.)

what paradoxical that the induced state in *Perilla* leaves themselves appears indestructible. Attempts by Zeevaart (1958) to remove it were completely unsuccessful, for after various treatments the capacity to bring about flowering was retained. The treatments included exposure of the detached leaves to continuous light of low or high intensity, solutions of a synthetic auxin (naphthalene-acetic acid), high temperatures (up to 5 hours at 42° C), and the respiratory inhibitors dinitrophenol and sodium azide. As long as a leaf survived, so did its induced state. However, Lam and Leopold (1961) have recently obtained results indicating that, under certain circumstances, the induced state in a *Perilla* leaf may be gradually lost.

One of the most curious properties of the induced state in *Xanthium* is its quantitative nature. This is not to be confused with the phenomenon previously mentioned (for example, in Biloxi soybean) in which eventual reversion to the vegetative state is preceded by an "amount" of flowering proportional to the inductive treatment. In *Xanthium,* too, the intensity of flowering is quantitatively related to the inductive treatment (for example, Salisbury, 1955), but since intact plants do not revert, they merely continue flower development at a very slow rate if the initial induction treatment is minimal. F. L. Naylor (1941) compared the development of plants under repeated short days with that of others given only a single short day and then placed in long-day conditions. In the former, inflorescences with all flower parts complete were evident after 13 days, and the seeds were almost mature within a month. The second group did not show complete flower development until over two months from the single short day, but the slow progress toward fruiting gave no sign of stopping before the experiment was discontinued, shortly thereafter. This kind of observation seems much more difficult to explain than a mere reversion to vegetative growth. The latter could be due to exhaustion of florigen or, as in *Perilla,* of the capacity to produce it, but maintenance of a long-lived but low "steady state" of flowering cannot be visualized on this basis. In a sense it is analogous to the fractional induction described in Chapter Three, except that in fractional induction there is no morphological or anatomical change after the first, subminimal, treatment.

There is little to be added here to the description of the state induced by vernalization covered in the preceding chapter. Perhaps its most remarkable property, akin to the way in which a small leaf area brings about flowering in a large plant, is the way in which only a small portion (the meristem) need be vernalized. Present evidence, however, does not point to the existence of a transmissible stimulus, and the vernalized state probably occurs only in tissues actually derived from the cells originally treated. Like photoperiodic induction, the effect of cold treatment is quantitative and "fractional" under certain conditions.

THE BIOCHEMISTRY OF INDUCTION

What of the cellular and biochemical changes involved in induction and the final flowering response? These changes must be understood if knowledge of the physiology of flowering is to be more than superficial, but up to the present time very little evidence sufficient to answer the question has been uncovered. The subject cannot be dismissed so briefly, however, if only because many investigators have tried to remedy the situation and one should be aware of their attempts.

As indicated in Chapters Two and Three, photoperiodic induction is a highly complex process. In SDP, at least, it is often regarded as comprising several steps, or "partial processes"—the first high-intensity light process, the dark process, the low-intensity light process by which the dark process can be inhibited, and the second high-intensity light process. To these can also be added florigen synthesis (marking the attainment of the induced state), followed by florigen translocation, and then the changes in the meristem (see, for example, Bonner, 1959a; Bonner and Liverman, 1953; Liverman, 1955). This analysis is more appropriate for some plants than for others, and none has been studied enough to disclose the nature of any of the partial processes, except perhaps the two involving high light-intensity. These may be photosynthetic, as we have seen in Chapter Two, and thus supply both energy for the other changes and carbohydrates with which the florigen moves. LDP have been less amenable to such an analysis, particularly with the evidence of both promoting and inhibiting actions due to the leaves and both of which may be affected by light and darkness. One of the few consistent observations is that the dark (and low light-intensity) processes in most plants studied appear at least to have the red, far-red reversible system in common, but its biochemical function is unknown. Again, the role of endogenous rhythms is uncertain.

Many specific mechanisms have been proposed for various processes in induction, mostly involving transformations and interactions of hypothetical substances. As Lang (1952) has pointed out, they are often little more than generalized restatements of particular data. Since expositions of these hypotheses abound in the reviews and papers cited, no attempt will be made to represent them here. Instead we will briefly consider some of the general areas of investigation involved.

One of the earliest and still most favored ideas is that auxin plays a major part in photoperiodic induction and flower initiation. The possibility that induction might be caused by a change in auxin content was tested by Chailakhyan and Zhdanova (1938); they concluded that this was unlikely since auxin content in a number of plants was greater on long than on short days, irrespective of whether they were LDP or SDP. More recent work of the kind has confirmed their general conclusions (see Hillman and Galston, 1961; Doorenbos and Wellensiek, 1959), but a major problem is the multiplicity of auxins as well as other growth-promoting and growth-inhibiting substances in plants; it is difficult to be sure that all the relevant compounds have been assayed in a given investigation. Thus changes in one or another identified or unidentified substance may or may not be correlated either with a change from one photoperiod to another or with flowering response, but are not easily interpretable as the cause of flowering (Cooke, 1954; Vlitos and Meudt, 1954).

A study by Harada and Nitsch (1959a), in which paper chromatography was used to separate and help identify various compounds, illustrates the complexity of the situation. They followed changes in the amounts of growth substances extractable from an LDP, an SDP, and a vernalizable plant at various times during or after induction. In each plant there was a number (3 to 6, perhaps more) of active substances; the levels of some changed in such a way as to suggest that they might be the cause of the developmental changes rather than being merely correlated with them. These results are only suggestive at present, but intensive pursuit of this kind of work may eventually clarify the relation of auxins and similar substances to flower initiation.

Another approach is shown in the work of Konishi (1956). His studies of auxin level in several LDP (*Silene, Rudbeckia, Spinacia*) were based entirely on biological assays without previous separation of possible multiple substances, but he also considered enzyme systems that might be involved in the synthesis and destruction of the known auxin, indoleacetic acid. Increased activity of the former and reduced activity of the latter were associated with the "bolting" —rapid stem elongation—characteristic of flowering in many LDP; evidence is lacking, however, that these changes actually cause bolting and flowering.

Some indirect evidence of a role for auxin in flowering has been obtained with radiations believed to affect auxin concentration, including both ultraviolet (UV) and x-rays. As early as 1887, Julius Sachs concluded that UV promoted flowering, since both *Tropaeolum* (*nasturtium*) and *Lepidium* flowered readily in sunlight filtered through water but not through a colorless solution of quinine, which absorbs UV. The flowering of *Linum usitatissimum* (flax) and *Statice bonduelli* is greatly hastened by exposure to a minute or two of intense UV each day, according to von Denffer and Schlitt (1951). Supporting von Denffer's (1950) idea that auxin is a major inhibitor of flowering, they concluded that this effect of UV was due to an inactivation of auxin within the plants, and believe it explains the rapid flowering occasionally encountered at high altitudes where more UV reaches the vegetation. Many other plants tested, however, did not respond in this way. An example of the promotion of flowering by low x-ray doses, known to reduce auxin synthesis, is reported by Leopold and Thimann (1949); flowering in Wintex barley was increased by over 20 percent after three weekly treatments with 25 roentgens.

Further indirect evidence comes from the effects of gravity. Geotropic stimulation is known to cause a changed pattern of auxin distribution in plants, although the mechanism is unknown (see Audus, 1959; Leopold, 1955); it can also hasten flowering. The Cabezona variety of pineapple (*Ananas comosus*) can be brought to flower at any time by bending the stem into a horizontal position and keeping it bent for as few as three days; assays confirm the assumption that this treatment results in auxin redistribution (van

Overbeek and Cruzado, 1948). In certain soybean varieties also, keeping the stem apex bent over causes earlier flowering, which Fisher (1957) again attributes to auxin redistribution, presumably a lower level at the older nodes resulting from an accumulation at the apex.

Hypotheses on the role of auxin in flowering have been based largely on the effects of externally applied auxins and related compounds, to be considered in the next chapter, rather than on the kind of work described above. Neither type of evidence has lent itself to any simple interpretation. In addition to hypotheses in which auxin simply inhibits or promotes flowering, one of the most elaborate schemes suggested relates its action directly to the red, far-red reversible system (see Liverman, 1955). The evidence is derived largely from work with processes other than flowering, and the "morphogenetic photocycle," as the scheme has been called, has not been widely accepted, at least in its original form (see Lang, 1959; Hillman, 1959c).

The gibberellins, a class of compounds to be discussed in the next chapter, can cause flowering in many LDP when applied externally. So far there is little information on whether the control of the level of these substances by photoperiod or temperature may explain certain flowering responses. Some of the Harada and Nitsch (1959) results are suggestive of a change in gibberellin levels following induction, but the bioassay used was relatively unspecific. A more specific assay was used by Lang (1960), whose preliminary results show a higher gibberellin level in induced than in non-induced annual *Hyoscyamus*. That this may be a cause of flowering rather than simply correlated with it is indicated by the fact that the increase shows up soon after induction and is less pronounced after flowering is well under way. This sort of work is now developing rapidly; and, as mentioned earlier about research on the red, far-red pigment, what is reported here may well be obsolete by publication.

The role of respiratory systems has also been studied. Elliott and Leopold (1952), for example, following oxygen uptake in leaf tissues of certain SDP and LDP, concluded that respiration rate increased in the former and decreased in the latter with photo-induction, whereas rates in two daylength-indifferent plants were dependent on the total light given. Whether such correlations are general, and what their significance might be, is unknown. The fact that various well-known respiratory poisons, including cyanide, azide, and fluoride, may inhibit the dark period induction (Naka-yama, 1958, on *Pharbitis nil*) does not afford any special insight into the processes involved, but indicates simply that normal respiration is required to support them. This is true also of ver-nalization, at least on the basis of the oxygen-level and sugar-feeding experiments mentioned in the previous chapter.

There has been a series of investigations on the fixation of carbon dioxide in darkness, particularly by *Kalanchoë*, since photo-period influences its time-course and intensity in a manner sug-gestive of the effect on flowering. In addition other work has shown that exclusion of CO_2 during dark periods can reduce the induction of several SDP. These results are reviewed by Kunitake *et al.* (1957), who concluded from their own experiments with radioactive tracer techniques that short-day induction of *Kalanchoë* affected not the proportion of CO_2 fixed in various compounds but only the total amount. This conclusion, together with the fact that even this change occurs relatively late in induction, affords no support for the suggestion of a specific significance for dark CO_2 fixation in the inductive process.

The induced state in many plants has some of the character-istics of infection with a virus, or some other self-replicating entity. This is true both of photoperiodically induced *Xanthium*, in which florigen production appears to be autocatalytic, and, in a different way, of vernalization in those plants in which the vernalized state is maintained in all cells descended from those originally treated. Unfortunately this stimulating hypothesis of flowering as a virus disease has as yet no direct evidence in its favor. Changes in the levels of both ribonucleic and desoxyribonucleic acids during and following photoinduction have been observed (Gulich, 1960, and bibliography therein), but all attempts to show qualitative dif-ferences between the nucleic acids or proteins of induced and non-induced plants have been unsuccessful (see Bonner and Liverman, 1953; Bonner, 1959b). However, some indirect evidence has been obtained by the use of compounds believed to inhibit nucleic acid synthesis. Hess (1959) found that 2-thiouracil given during the vernalization of *Streptocarpus* could reduce or abolish flower initiation without affecting vegetative growth; 5-fluorouracil is reported to inhibit photoperiodic induction in *Xanthium* in a manner possibly suggestive of an effect on the synthesis or effectiveness of the flowering hormone (Salisbury and Bonner, 1960). But 2-thiouracil also causes a strong inhibition of induction in another SDP, hemp (*Cannabis sativa*); careful histological observations suggest that this action and, by inference, those above are due to a general effect on the differentiation capacities of the meristem rather than to a specific effect on flowering (Heslop-Harrison, 1960).

A question of fundamental importance concerning photoperiodic induction was recently raised by R. M. Sachs on the basis of his and other work with LSDP (see Sachs, 1959). It has been widely assumed that the basic induction process in both LDP and SDP is alike, there being at least two grounds for this assumption. One is the participation of the red, far-red system in both types and the other is the apparent equivalence of florigen in both types, at least among many closely related plants. But Sachs points out that in the LSDP *Cestrum nocturnum* (night-blooming jasmine) long- and short-day induction appear to differ considerably. The product of long-day induction is not translocated from the treated leaves; short-day induction following long-day induction, however, gives rise to a translocatable flowering hormone. Further, the sequence of long- and short-day induction is not reversible for any plants requiring both—in LSDP the former must precede the latter, whereas in SLDP the reverse is true. Thus if one assumes that long-day induction in both LSDP and SLDP (as well as in simple LDP) controls the same step in a series of reactions, one then suspects that the short-day induction step in LSDP is not equivalent to that in SLDP. Similarly, assuming that short-day induction in both types (as well as in SDP) is the same, then the long-day induction in the two types must differ. In addition to indicating that short- and long-day induction may affect different processes, Sachs suggests that "we should be wary of the assumption that LD induction affects the same stage of synthesis of the floral stimulus in every LDP (the same doubt exists with regard to SD induction in all SDP)." The question will be finally answered only by a complete understanding of the biochemistry involved, which may take many years. The logic of Sachs's analysis warns that the answer will not be simple, and may also be different for different plants.

CONCLUDING REMARKS

An attempt at some sort of evaluation is desirable here, if only to avoid ending on a note of complete confusion. Some of the views to be expressed differ greatly from those held by other writers, who also differ among themselves; anyone seriously concerned with theoretical interpretations should consult various reviews cited earlier.

The "all-or-none," qualitative character of both floral initiation and photoperiodic induction has been widely stressed (for example, Lang, 1952). In the writer's opinion, it is a questionable concept. Admittedly, there are situations in which one either sees or does not see a floral primordium, so that the final judgment is either "flowering" or "vegetative." The same could be said, however, about the growth or nongrowth of a piece of tissue; at the lower limit of the technique used, one either detects growth or does not, yet there is no general opinion that growth is an all-or-none phenomenon. Bonner (1959a), accepting the photoperiodic response as in a sense quantitative, nevertheless goes on, "each bud and each plant is either reproductive or vegetative." Logically, this is true enough. But in developmental, morphological terms, one has only to consider work like that of Harder (1948) on *Kalanchoë* to realize that there can be a continuum between obviously vegetative and obviously reproductive growth.

One origin of the all-or-none view may be an overemphasis on flower initiation (although such studies usually involve some degree of development) with too little attention to the fact that optimum flower development often requires a continuation of the inducing conditions. A good illustration of this common situation was recently given by Zabka (1961) working with *Amaranthus caudatus*. At a certain age this is a very sensitive SDP; when older, it initiates flowers even under long days. Under any circumstances, however, inflorescence development and fruiting are strongly favored by short days, no matter how initiation came about.

Another major support of the all-or-none view has been the fact that, in SDP for example, flowering does not occur at daylengths above the critical but does occur at lower values. This thus seemed to represent a sharp, qualitative cut-off in the curve of response versus daylength, but only on the assumption that daylengths above the critical had no other effect than to be noninductive. Work mentioned in Chapter Three, however, indicates now that such daylengths are often positively antiinductive, not merely ineffective, and that this antagonistic effect is quantitatively related to the amount by which the noninductive daylength exceeds the critical. While no generalization is likely to hold for all plants, it is possible that the processes involved in induction proceed continuously, and that only the ratio of the rates of, say, two or more of them differs under different daylengths. The critical daylength would then be that value at which the ratio neither promotes nor inhibits the train of events finally leading to flowering.

Many of the subjects touched on in the preceding chapters, including the question of the degree of difference between the structure of vegetative and floral meristems, bear on this sort of problem, but cannot be enlarged upon now. The relevance of such theoretical considerations to more concrete questions is largely in the suggestion that flowering does not represent a sudden change, some sort of developmental "quantum-jump," but is probably under controls similar to those affecting vegetative growth, to the small degree that these are understood.

Consider, for instance, the nature of floral stimuli. That something moves between induced and noninduced parts of a plant, or between grafted plants, cannot be doubted. Movement of active substances from vegetative to reproductive tissue is also highly probable. In physiological terms, then, both florigen and antiflorigen appear to be valid concepts, but in the absence of extracted samples one can only speculate as to their nature and whether they are the same in all plants. In the light of the considerations above, it appears extremely unlikely to the writer that florigens, whether simple substances or as complex as a virus, are likely to be specific floral hormones in the sense that they are involved only in the processes of floral initiation and development but no others. Julius Sachs's concept of specific organ-forming substances has not stood the test of experimentation, since most vegetative systems studied indicate that particular aspects of development can be controlled by the concentrations and interactions of substances that affect many other processes as well. A few examples will be helpful here.

The use of the auxin indoleacetic acid in rooting cuttings is well known; in addition, much of the rooting behavior of cuttings can be explained in terms of their auxin content and sensitivity. Yet it is also known that the same compound plays a major role in other developmental processes having nothing to do with root initiation, so that it would be grossly misleading to call it "rhizogen" (root-maker). That development is controlled by the balance of various substances common to many processes is strikingly illustrated by the work of Skoog and Tsui (1948) and Miller and Skoog (1953). Tobacco stem segments grown in aseptic culture produce roots if supplied with a particular level of auxin and shoots if supplied with another substance, adenine. Both compounds together cause the production of more or less disorganized callus tissue; but increasing the adenine again leads to shoot formation, whereas increasing the auxin leads to root formation. Thus the balance of auxin and adenine controls the production of roots or shoots in this system. Adenine, as a component of the nucleic acids and many respiratory co-enzymes, is probably present in every living cell; the many roles of auxin have already been mentioned (see Audus, 1959).

A simpler example of control by an unspecific substance was found by Wetmore (1953), who studied the development of young fern apices in aseptic culture. The first few leaves produced by ferns, as by many other plants, may differ considerably from the later ones, being characteristically "juvenile" in some way; the ferns in question (*Todea, Adiantum*) have juvenile leaves with few or no divisions, whereas the older leaves are deeply lobed. In culture, mere variation of the sucrose content of the medium suffices to bring about almost any degree of "juvenility" or "maturity" in leaf shape, with the lowest sucrose level giving the least lobed leaves. Thus the normal leaf progression, regarded as a fundamental developmental property of the meristem and one of considerable evolutionary significance, is susceptible to regulation by a substance that presumably serves merely as a general energy source. This result may have more than illustrative value here. If, as Philipson (1949) suggests, the reproductive apex simply represents a normal later stage in the ontogeny of the shoot, as does the transition from juvenile to mature foliage, then perhaps a local increase in carbohydrates may play a central role in flowering itself.

One further study on vegetative growth should be considered since it bears comparison with the quantitative yet long-lived induced state which seems so puzzling in *Xanthium*. The reader whose sensibilities were disturbed by "flowering as a virus disease" will have to make the best of another similar analogy, this time to the plant disease crown-gall. In many ways resembling cancer in animals, crown-gall is brought about by a bacterium; following infection, the tissues become tumorous, growing rapidly in a disorganized fashion, and continue to do so even when the bacteria are no longer present. Pieces of such bacteria-free tissue grow rapidly in culture on a simple mineral medium with sucrose and a few vitamins, whereas normal callus tissue from the same plant fails to grow under the same conditions. Braun (1958) has been able to make a whole series of tissue clones intermediate between typical crown-gall and typical normal tissues in their growth rate on the basic medium. This was done by letting the bacterial infection proceed for different lengths of time before a heat treatment that stops it without harming the tissue. In order to make normal tissue grow as fast as fully tumorous crown-gall tissue in culture, one must add to the basic medium 6-furfuryl amino purine, guanylic and cytidylic acids, asparagine, glutamine, inositol, and naphthaleneacetic acid. If the tissue has been exposed to infection for a short time, the first compound may be omitted; if it has been exposed for a longer time, the first four may be omitted, without reducing the rate below that of the fully tumorous tissue.

Each strain of tissue maintains its particular nutritional requirements in culture and does not revert to normal. Braun concludes that "a series of quite distinct, but well-defined, growth-substance-synthesizing systems becomes progressively activated" during the crown-gall induction. In short, a quantitative gradation exists as a result of several qualitative changes in metabolism. Perhaps photoperiodic induction in some plants is a process of this kind, with many intermediate stages, and not a unitary process at all.

With such work as background one might envision florigen as either a single substance, or a combination of substances, normally occurring in many plant cells, but frequently present in insufficient quantities or improper balance for the meristem to proceed to reproductive development. If production in another part of the plant, the leaf, is susceptible to modification by day-length, there will be evidence of photoperiodically induced, trans-locatable floral stimuli or inhibitors. When such production is not under photoperiodic control, the stimuli or inhibitors may still be demonstrable. There is no a priori reason to assume that these are the same for all plants simply because they appear to be so in certain closely related forms. (They do not appear to be so in all; see Zeevaart, 1958.) On the other hand, work with the gib-berellins indicates that the same compound can cause flowering in many unrelated LDP, although gibberellins themselves cannot be florigen, as will be indicated in the next chapter.

The fact that floral stimuli to the present have proved non-extractable, and are transferable only by grafting, has been used as supporting evidence for the "virus" concept (see Bonner, 1959b) in spite of the fact that many viruses are easily extracted and transmitted by other means. It is at least as likely that the com-pounds involved are simply unstable under most extraction tech-niques. Still another possibility is precisely that florigen activity is either due to a particular balance of substances or, as suggested by Went (1959), is the reflection "of rhythmic concentration changes" of one or more substances. In either case, extraction of the right combination would prove extremely difficult, and move-ment through a nonliving gap might disrupt the relationships involved even though the substances themselves were stable.

The reader may well protest that the intent of this section, "to avoid ending on a note of complete confusion," has been badly betrayed. In answer, the entire point here is that there is no con-fusion, only ignorance. There are undoubtedly many growth-regulating substances and systems of which we know nothing as yet, and which will change present attitudes as much as work with the red, far-red system or the gibberellins is changing those of the past decades. Therefore a comprehensive statement on the subject of this chapter is not only impossible but undesirable, since it would have to assume that all parts of the puzzle are now in hand and simply need putting together. All of the concepts in the literature are valuable to the extent that they are useful as working hypotheses, but they should not be mistaken for anything else. What we need is more of the missing pieces, wherever or however they may be found.

chapter six ▸ Chemical Control

of Flowering

Attempts to bring about or prevent flowering by the application of chemicals are carried on for both practical and theoretical reasons. The former are self-evident, the latter hardly less so. As already indicated, studies on the mechanism of induction have included work with various metabolic inhibitors, which will not be considered further here. More attention has been paid to the effects of naturally occurring compounds and of other substances that modify plant growth; variations in the supply of various minerals have also been studied with respect to flowering.

A major motive of this kind of work has been the hope of discovering compounds, either naturally occurring or synthetic, with florigen activity. Although there have been reports of success from time to time, none of these has as yet proved valid. Either the work has been unrepeatable or the substance in question has not fulfilled the criteria for florigen. Drawing on the previous chapter, the minimal requirement for such activity is the ability to bring about flowering both in LDP under short days and in SDP under long days, as well as in cold-requiring but unvernalized plants. In addition, if the substance is to be considered a true (naturally occurring) florigen, it should of course be produced only under inductive conditions. It is well to keep these criteria in mind, since the effects of the first class of compounds to be considered are dramatic enough to be misleading in this regard.

99

THE GIBBERELLINS

The single most striking property of the gibberellins, besides the effects on flowering to be discussed, is their ability to cause greatly accelerated growth in intact plants. This is evident mainly in the stem, but occurs also in other parts and is especially obvious in certain "dwarf" varieties. No other group of compounds, including the auxins, is known to have such effects on a wide variety of intact plants. Gibberellins also act on many of the same phenomena affected by red and far-red light. Such action is not consistently in one direction—in some cases, such as seed germination, gibberellins appear to mimic the effect of red, but in others (for example, stem elongation) they act in the same direction as far-red. It has thus been suggested that gibberellins may be involved in the action of the red, far-red system, but none of the specific hypotheses proposed is as yet sufficiently grounded to be considered here.

Several gibberellins have been isolated from higher plants, but the group was originally discovered as products of a fungus (*Gibberella fujikuroi*) causing a rice disease characterized by excessive stem elongation. They are complex compounds that can be regarded as derivatives of the hydrocarbon fluorene with lactone, hydroxyl, and other substituents. The detailed structures of some of them, notably gibberellin A_3 (gibberellic acid), are fairly well established. Much of the work to be discussed has been done with gibberellic acid, but other gibberellins have been studied as well, and the general term "gibberellin" will often be used. Research on the gibberellins has been pursued for several decades in Japan, but became known outside that country only relatively recently. The first generally available review, by Stowe and Yamaki in 1957, has since been followed by others, and all should be consulted for a thorough knowledge of this rapidly developing topic (Brian, 1959; Phinney and West, 1960; Stowe and Yamaki, 1960; Wittwer and Bukovac, 1958). For an excellent discussion of gibberellin and flowering, see Lang and Reinhard (1961).

The first thorough publication on gibberellin and flowering was that of Lang (1957), showing that a few drops of a dilute solution (chiefly gibberellic acid) given repeatedly to the growing point or leaves brought about flowering of unvernalized biennial

Hyoscyamus, carrot (*Daucus carota*), and several other biennials, all under long-day conditions (see Fig. 6-1). Several LDP kept on short days, including annual *Hyoscyamus, Samolus parviflorus,* and *Silene armeria,* also flowered in response to such treatment. No promotion of flowering occurred in the SDP *Xanthium* and Biloxi soybeans kept on long days. These experiments were conducted with gibberellins of fungal origin. Similar results on both *Samolus* and biennial *Hyoscyamus* were later obtained with extracts of wild-cucumber (*Echinocystis*) seeds, known to be rich higher-plant sources of gibberellins (Lang *et al.,* 1957). Evidently, then, gibberellin can substitute for the cold requirement of certain vernalizable plants and for the long-day requirement of certain LDP, but not for the short-day requirement of SDP. This general conclusion still appears valid, but requires expansion.

Vernalization or long-day requirements have not been successfully replaced by gibberellin in all plants tested. One reason for this may be the known difference in activity, for a given plant, among the various gibberellins themselves (see Phinney and West, 1960) well illustrated by Fig. 6-2. Possibly plants that have not responded so far will do so when other gibberellins are tried. In the "classical" experimental objects for vernalization studies, the winter cereals, gibberellic acid can hasten flowering in unvernalized seedlings, but only when applied at a particular stage; in addition to flowering, which is often abnormal or abortive, other changes in meristem development occur (Caso *et al.,* 1960; Koller *et al.,* 1960; Purvis, 1960). Further lack of exact correspondence between gibberellin effects and vernalization is found in the work of Sarkar (1958), discussed in the next chapter, showing that optimum sensitivity to gibberellin or to cold treatment need not occur at the same stage of development. Moore and Bonde (1958) have observed that gibberellic acid actually devernalizes or prevents vernalization in a variety of *Pisum,* depending on whether it is applied after or before the cold treatment.

It is important to realize that, at least so far, all the LDP in which gibberellin does replace long days are those in which flowering is associated with "bolting"—the rapid elongation of the axis from the almost stemless "rosette" of leaves characteristic of the vegetative condition. In caulescent LDP, having elongated stems even when vegetative, gibberellin apparently cannot bring about

Fig. 6-1. Substitution of gibberellic acid (GA) for cold treatment in the flowering of the biennial, carrot (*Daucus carota*). *Left to right:* controls on long days only; long days plus GA, no cold treatment; long days plus previous cold treatment, no GA. (Photograph from Lang [1957], courtesy of Dr. A. Lang, California Institute of Technology.)

Fig. 6-2. Effects of various gibberellins on flowering of the LDP lettuce (*Lactuca sativa* var. Grand Rapids) on short days. *From left to right:* controls (vegetative), and gibberellins A_1 (flowering), A_2, A_3, and A_4. Plants were treated with a total of 4 applications of 10 microliters of 10^{-3} M solutions at weekly intervals starting when 6 to 8 true leaves were present. (Photograph courtesy of Dr. M. J. Bukovac, Michigan State University.)

flowering. Examples of such plants are Roman nettle (*Urtica pilulifera*) and enchanter's nightshade (*Circaea lutetiana*) (Lona, 1956). Since most of the widely studied LDP are rosette plants, the notion that gibberellin promotes flowering in all LDP has been current but is probably untrue. Not even all rosette plants tested have proved responsive.

Most of the other situations in which gibberellin substitutes for long days involve stem elongation. It causes flowering in the LSDP *Bryophyllum crenatum* grown under short days, thus satisfying the long-day requirement; this again is a matter of bringing about bolting (Bünsow *et al.*, 1958). Another example is its action on strawberry plants, in which it causes runner initiation, petiole elongation, and flowering inhibition. These effects are all similar to those of long days, and the postulated flower-inhibiting, growth-promoting substance produced on long days may be related to gibberellin. (Thompson and Guttridge, 1959; see also Chapter Five in this volume.)

The action of gibberellin on stem development may well be primary, with the promotion of flowering in rosette plants—both LDP and biennials—an indirect result. Lang (1957), for example, noted that although flower initiation in the rosette plants studied occurred with the start of bolting under normal conditions—long days, or vernalization followed by long days—bolting in gibberellin-treated plants generally preceded flower initiation. In some rosette plants, gibberellin causes bolting only, without flowering (Lona, 1956; see Wittwer and Bukovac, 1958). In many rosette plants, normal flowering occurs only if the environmental requirements are partially satisfied (see Brian, 1959; Chouard, 1960). Anatomical investigations by Sachs, Lang, and collaborators (Sachs *et al.*, 1959, 1960) show that the early effect of gibberellin treatment on several rosette plants is the activation of the "subapical meristem," somewhat below the growing apex. The increased cell divisions in this area are largely transverse; this, plus the subsequent cell elongation, results in rapid stem growth. Gibberellin can also completely reverse the effects of the complex growth-regulating compound Amo-1618, which causes a dwarfed or rosette habit in normally caulescent plants such as *Chrysanthemum* by inhibiting the activity of the subapical meristem. While such work bears no direct relationship to flowering, it strengthens the view that gibberellin may indirectly remove some inhibition on flowering through its direct effect on stem growth.

Gibberellin may either promote or inhibit later flower development in SDP, but is entirely unable to bring about initiation under noninductive conditions. In addition to the work already mentioned, a striking example of its ineffectiveness occurs with the species *Chrysanthemum morifolium*. In those varieties requiring only cold treatment to flower, irrespective of daylength, gibberellic acid can cause flowering. In those that are SDP, however, it does not (Harada and Nitsch, 1959b). In *Kalanchoë*, gibberellin reduces the flowering of plants kept on short days, although it promotes vegetative growth. In spite of this, the effect is not identical with that of long days since it makes no difference whether or not the gibberellin-treated leaf lies between the short-day (induced) leaf and the growing point (Harder and Bünsow, 1956, 1957).

At least two detailed studies on *Xanthium* have appeared. Both agree that gibberellic acid cannot cause flowering under long-day conditions; it can, however, increase the flowering response to a limited number of short-day cycles. Greulach and Haesloop (1958) obtained such results with intact plants; Lincoln and Hamner (1958), on the other hand, found this effect only in de-budded plants, and concluded that the compound acted by increasing the capacity of the young leaves to store the flowering stimulus.

Flowering in a strain of the duckweed *Lemna perpusilla* may take place under any daylength or may require short days, depending upon factors to be discussed later. In both situations, however, gibberellin can completely abolish flowering at levels that promote vegetative growth, although other associated morphogenetic effects prevent this from being considered a specific inhibition of flowering (Hillman, 1960).

In summary, the gibberellins have already contributed greatly to the study of flowering: they are the first compounds discovered with which many kinds of plants can be brought to flower almost at will. Further understanding of the way in which they fully or partially satisfy requirements for long-day or cold treatments, at least in rosette plants, will be of great value. The closeness of their relation to flowering, as compared with other developmental processes such as stem elongation, is still in doubt, and the results with SDP indicate that no gibberellin so far tested can be considered a florigen. However, there is good preliminary evidence that native gibberellin levels in certain plants increase as a result of treatments leading to flowering, and such changes may be part of the normal mechanism involved (Chapter Five).

AUXINS, AUXIN ANTAGONISTS, AND OTHER GROWTH REGULATORS

Since auxins were widely known long before the gibberellins, there has been more work on their effects on flowering. In addition to auxins, one must consider also the effects of auxin antagonists. This broad term is used here to cover any substances believed to act in a manner opposed to that of auxin. Such action may be exerted through a molecular structure sufficiently similar to that of an auxin to interact with the same biochemical site, yet not sufficiently similar to participate further in whatever system auxin normally acts. Such an auxin antagonist, competitive with auxin molecules, would be a true "antiauxin." Other auxin antagonists may act by interfering with native auxin synthesis, by blocking the transport of auxin from the site of action, or by interfering with the effectiveness of auxin in some other way. Finally, many other organic compounds effective as growth regulators—capable of modifying development in various ways—have also been tested on flowering. All of these topics will be considered briefly. None of the results so far has provided much clear information on flowering, since most of the evidence suggests that the effects obtained are extremely indirect.

As noted in the preceding chapter, studies on the changes in native auxin levels associated with flower induction are inconclusive. In considering the effects of applied auxins, one should bear in mind that these frequently cause all kinds of abnormalities in growth, depending upon the concentrations (see, for example, Audus, 1959; Leopold, 1955). With respect to auxin effects on flowering, comparison of earlier reviews (for example, Lang, 1952; Bonner and Liverman, 1953) with more recent ones such as Leopold's (1958) or the excellent critical article by Lang (1959) indicates a marked decline in the certainty with which any general statement can be made.

There have been indications that auxin treatment promotes flowering in LDP and inhibits in SDP. The results of some of the papers on this question should illustrate the general uncertainty.

In experiments by Liverman and Lang (1956) flower initiation in annual *Hyoscyamus* and *Silene* was promoted by the auxin indoleacetic acid (IAA) under conditions in which the controls remained vegetative. These, however, were "threshold" conditions—supplementary light of intensities not quite sufficient to cause flowering by itself was used to extend the photoperiod beyond its critical value. No auxin promotions were observed under strict short-day conditions. Promotion of flowering in another LDP, Wintex barley, has been observed by Leopold and Thimann (1949). This effect was obtained under inductive conditions and appears to be simply a promotion of later inflorescence development. Note that in the same experiments (see Chapter Five) x-irradiation, which may reduce the auxin level, also increased flowering.

In the SDP *Xanthium,* Bonner and Thurlow (1949) reported that application of the auxins IAA, naphthaleneacetic acid, or 2,4-dichlorophenoxyacetic acid (2,4-D) to cuttings or to leaves of intact plants prevented the flowering response to short days. This effect was opposed by the auxin antagonists 2,4-dichloroanisole and 2,3,5-triiodobenzoic acid (TIBA). The antagonists themselves, under threshold conditions—night interruptions barely sufficient to keep the controls vegetative—caused the initiation of "flowerlike buds," which, however, did not develop into flowers (Bonner, 1949).

Auxin inhibitions of flowering in *Xanthium* have been studied further by Lockhart and Hamner (1954) who showed that IAA increased both the magnitude and consistency of the inhibition caused by a second dark period following the inductive night (Chapter Two). Additional data on auxin inhibition in both *Xanthium* and Biloxi soybean are provided in Hamner and Nanda (1956). Salisbury (1955), again with *Xanthium,* found that auxin inhibited flowering only if applied before translocation of the "flowering stimulus" appeared to be completed—that is, before the end of the period during which removal of the induced leaves could reduce the flowering response. If applied later, it promoted flower development, particularly under reduced light intensities or in the absence of actively growing buds. Inhibitions by IAA applied before and during the inductive dark period have also been reported in the SDP *Pharbitis* (Nakayama, 1958), although earlier work showed promotions under similar conditions (Nakayama and Kikuchi, 1956).

One of the few plants in which auxins have a major effect on flowering is the pineapple (*Ananas comosus*). As noted in Chapter

Five, one variety flowers in response to geotropic stimulation, an effect that has been ascribed to a change in native auxin distribution. In addition, a number of varieties can be made to flower by applications of synthetic auxins such as naphthaleneacetic acid (NAA) or 2,4-D. IAA appears to be a native auxin in pineapple, and, paradoxically, it has been suggested that NAA may act in this situation as an auxin antagonist—an antiauxin, in fact, competing with the native IAA—and that flowering may result from a lowering of the effective level of the native auxin (Bonner and Liverman, 1953; Gowing, 1956). Whatever the explanation, the phenomenon itself is easily repeatable and of considerable economic importance; sprays of synthetic auxins are used to schedule flowering, and hence fruiting, in commercial plantations (see van Overbeek, 1952; Leopold, 1958).

Flowering in pineapple can be brought about also by several compounds structurally unrelated to auxins, including β-hydroxyethylhydrazine, acetylene, and ethylene (see Leopold, 1958). Indeed, pineapple is not the only plant in which ethylene can cause flowering. Khudairi and Hamner (1954b) found that ethylene chlorohydrin vapor caused flower initiation in *Xanthium* plants under 16-hour photoperiods. As with the auxin-antagonist results mentioned previously, the experiments were carried out under threshold conditions, with supplementary light of low intensities.

The mechanism of ethylene action on flowering or any other plant process is unknown, but there is some evidence that it acts as an auxin antagonist, possibly reducing the native auxin content. If this is so, then its effects on both *Xanthium* and pineapple are in accord with the hypothesis that synthetic auxins act as antiauxins for the pineapple, and the whole set of observations can be used to support the hypothesis that, at least under certain conditions, flowering may occur after the lowering of a superoptimal auxin level. However, with the bits of evidence discussed in Chapter Five, this hypothesis remains highly speculative.

Auxin antagonists have provided another major difficulty in analyzing the auxin relationships to flower initiation. Certain compounds believed to be true antiauxins (such as 2,4-dichlorophenoxyisobutyric acid or 2,4-6-trichlorophenoxyacetic acid) and others that may rather inhibit auxin transport (such as 2,3,5-triiodobenzoic acid) promote flowering in annual *Hyoscyamus* under threshold conditions just as do several auxins. No convincing hypothesis about such results has yet been stated (see Lang, 1959).

Many growth regulators can speed or delay flowering somewhat under particular circumstances. These effects are usually minor and are also associated with equal or greater effects on vegetative growth. Occasionally, dramatic and at present inexplicable effects of particular compounds on particular plants are discovered, of which two examples will be cited. For further information, see Audus (1959) and Leopold (1958).

Furfuryl alcohol, a compound not previously known to have growth-regulating activity for higher plants and not obviously related to known growth regulators, promotes flowering and bolting in the LDP *Rudbeckia speciosa* under short days in the same way as does gibberellin (Nitsch and Harada, 1958). In one of the two experiments reported, some of the control plants flowered as well, so the conditions may have been close to threshold. Effects on other plants are unknown.

The compound N-metatolylphthalamic acid is one of a group of growth regulators that profoundly affects flowering as well as other processes in a number of plants. It is particularly effective in increasing flowering in the tomato (*Lycopersicon esculentum*), a daylength-indifferent plant, chiefly by increasing the number of flowers in each cluster. High doses may even cause the development of a large inflorescence at the apex, causing further vegetative growth to stop. Such promotions of inflorescence development appear to be due to temporary or permanent suppression of the branch that would otherwise arise beneath an inflorescence and compete with it, and are almost certainly not direct effects on flower initiation (Cordner and Hedges, 1959).

PLANT EXTRACTS OF VARIOUS KINDS

Many naturally occurring substances have been tested for possible flower-promoting activity, often as extracts of uncertain composition. No such work, other than that with gibberellins, has as yet been conspicuously successful, but it is well to consider some representative efforts.

An extract of the young inflorescence of a palm, *Washingtonia robusta*, apparently brought about flowering in *Xanthium* under long days in experiments by Bonner and Bonner (1948). Unfortunately their attempts to repeat this work, with inflorescence extracts from the same and other species of palm, were completely unsuccessful, so the result remains unexplained.

In 1951, Roberts also reported the extraction of a substance that induced flowering in *Xanthium* under long days. It appeared to be of a lipide nature and obtainable only from flowering, not vegetative, individuals of a number of species including *Xanthium* itself. Although attempts in several other laboratories have failed to confirm Roberts's results, a long-chain keto-alcohol with activity as an auxin antagonist can be prepared from certain plants by the procedures used (see Struckmeyer and Roberts, 1955). Its florigenic properties, however, remain as doubtful as those of the palm extract. An extract with weak but significant flower-promoting activity for *Xanthium* plants in long days has recently been prepared by careful lyophilization of *Xanthium* inflorescences. Only future work will decide whether this result will go the way of the others cited, but the initial report is very encouraging (Lincoln *et al.,* 1961).

In an extensive investigation on the development of a strawberry (*Fragaria*) variety, Sironval (1957) has reported that unsaponifiable lipide fractions from flowering plants promote flowering of those in the vegetative condition. In only a few experiments, however, are the untreated controls completely vegetative, and often the differences between control and treated series are discouragingly small. The active substances in the extracts may include Vitamin E, which is itself active in the strawberry-plant test, and certain unidentified sterols.

Flowering in at least one vernalizable variety of pea (*Pisum sativum*) can be promoted by first allowing the seeds to imbibe "diffusate" prepared from other pea seeds (Highkin, 1955). Like vernalization, such treatment results in flowering at a lower node than in the controls; in the data published, the node number to the first flower was about 20 in the controls to about 18 in the treated, but was highly significant statistically. By a "diffusate" is meant an extract prepared not by grinding seeds in water but simply by soaking them, intact, under sterile conditions for varying periods of time during which active substances diffuse out into the water. Such diffusates probably contain many metabolically important compounds. In the investigation cited, the effect on flowering was about the same whether the diffusate was made by soaking the seeds at 23° or at 4° C; since only the latter temperature would vernalize, the activity cannot be considered to represent a vernalin (Chapter Five).

MINERAL NUTRITION; MAJOR ELEMENTS

The question of the relationship between mineral nutrition and flowering is embodied more in practical lore, and less in experimental data, than almost any other aspect of flowering physiology. Because of this, relatively little can be said here. Not that such lore is necessarily incorrect, but it is usually uncertain and often extremely local. One reason is that distinctions between relatively specific effects on flowering and those simply associated with changes in vegetative growth are usually not made, as indeed they do not need to be, for many practical purposes. Thus one frequently finds that nutritional conditions that simply favor optimal growth will be recommended to increase flowering and fruiting.

Interestingly enough, one of the commonest examples of such practical lore is the opposite belief, that flowering may result from conditions causing poor vegetative growth or restraining growth in some way. Although this may be simply an inverse recognition of the fact that in many plants flowering and fruiting are associated with and may cause a reduction in vegetative growth (see Leopold *et al.*, 1959), there may be more to it. The clearest recent study on this question has nothing to do with mineral nutrition, but tends to confirm the view that, at least in certain plants, growth restraint can promote flowering. Kojima and Maeda (1958) studied a variety of radish (*Raphanus*) in which flowering is hastened by vernalization. In unvernalized seedlings, flowering and bolting were promoted by several treatments that greatly impeded the growth of the stem apex. The most effective was to imbed the upper part of the seedling for several days in gypsum; another was to immerse the seedlings in relatively concentrated sugar solutions, which inhibited growth osmotically. The mechanism by which a growth restraint might promote flowering is unknown, but the data seem clear and suggest that such notions are better tested than dismissed.

The suggestion that nitrogen nutrition plays an important role in the control of flowering and fruiting in a manner related to the considerations above was strongly supported, although not originated, by Kraus and Kraybill in 1918 (see Kraus, 1925). They concluded that fruitfulness in the tomato plant depended on the ratio of carbohydrate to nitrogen—the C/N ratio. Under a given light intensity (to supply the carbohydrates) and at a given temperature (which would govern the rate at which they are metabolized), the C/N ratio can obviously be controlled by controlling the nitrogen supply. In Kraus and Kraybill's experiments, a moderate ratio was favorable to flowering and fruiting, whereas a low ratio (high nitrogen) favored luxuriant vegetative growth but little reproductive development. This conclusion in generalized form was for a while inflated out of all proportion to the data supporting it, which appear to have been valid largely for the particular conditions used. However, one should note in fairness that Kraus and Kraybill were chiefly interested in later flower development and fruiting, not in flower initiation.

A more recent study by Wittwer and Teubner (1957), also on tomato, does not support the notion that high nitrogen favors vegetative growth at the expense of flowering. On the contrary, in solution culture the highest nitrogen level used gave the best flowering even under optimal temperature conditions. With respect to photoperiodic plants, El Hinnawy (1956) found that high nitrogen promoted earlier flowering in *Perilla* and *Kalanchoë* (both SDP) under inductive conditions, slowed it in mustard (*Brassica*) and dill, and had no effect on spinach (all three LDP) under inductive conditions. It had no effect on the photoperiodic response as such, and he concluded that the effects of nitrogen and other major element changes were highly indirect.

Eguchi *et al.* (1958) have studied the responses of some photoperiodic, vernalizable, or daylength-indifferent plants to levels of nitrogen and phosphate nutrition. They concluded that in the first two types the time of flowering, both chronologically and developmentally, was almost unaffected. In the daylength-indifferent plants, however, which included tomato, pepper (*Capsicum*), and eggplant (*Solanum*), there was a much greater effect. In a tomato variety, for example, flowering was earliest at the highest levels of nitrogen and phosphate used, with the first flower at node 8 or 9. Reducing either nitrogen or phosphate to the lowest level used delayed flowering to node 12 or 13 at the earliest. The authors proposed the interesting generalization that flowering in many tropical daylength-indifferent plants is far more dependent upon nutrition than it is in photoperiodic or vernalizable plants in which the environmental requirements have been satisfied. In this connection, note that Gott *et al.* (1955) found that a low nitrogen level delayed flowering in unvernalized or partially vernalized winter rye but hardly affected vernalized plants.

Although the literature on nutrition and flowering is more extensive than that presented here, these examples serve to indicate that, at least at present, there is no good evidence for a close relationship between a particular major element and flower initiation in most plants.

HEAVY METALS AND FLOWERING

There is some indication that iron nutrition may be more critically involved in photoperiodic induction. In a preliminary survey to see whether any of a large number of different mineral deficiencies would reduce the capacity of *Xanthium* to respond to short-day treatment, Smith *et al.* (1957) noted that iron, and possibly boron and magnesium deficiencies, had some effect. In further experiments they found that plants suffering from iron-deficiency symptoms failed to flower or flowered abnormally even when transferred to a high-iron medium after photoinduction. Such results are suggestive, although the inhibition of vegetative growth as well as the response to short-day leave them somewhat equivocal. Any special significance for iron in flower initiation has been questioned by Shibata (1959) in a brief investigation on rice (*Oryza sativa*).

A more clear-cut result was obtained by the writer (Hillman, 1961a), using a clone of the duckweed *Lemna perpusilla* growing in a well-chelated medium (see below). The plants were pretreated by growing them in media with various levels of iron for several days, given one (inductive) long night, and then all returned to a high-iron medium. Under these conditions, the flowering response to the single long night was essentially abolished by pretreatment with a level of iron not low enough to affect vegetative growth. In other words, the iron requirement for induction appeared to be higher than that for vegetative growth only. Whether this might be true also for other micronutrient elements in this plant, or whether it truly indicates a special role of iron in photoperiodic induction, is not yet clear. Yoshimura (1943) has reported promo-

A   **B**

Fig. 6-3. Duckweeds (*Lemna*) as experimental organisms for the study of flowering under highly controlled conditions. (*A*) An aseptic culture of *L. perpusilla*. (*B*) A group of *L. gibba*, showing anthers. (Photographs by Dr. J. H. Miller and Yale University Photographic Services.)

tion of flowering in another duckweed, *Spirodela*, by molybdenum deficiency. For a review of other early reports on duckweed flowering, see Hillman (1961a).

The writer has pursued evidence of important metal effects in photoperiodism originating in observations on the effects of chelating agents on the flowering of two species of *Lemna* (see Fig. 6-3). Chelating agents are compounds that form particularly stable complexes with many metal ions and thus affect their chemical reactivity. Many compounds of biological importance (for example, amino acids) are chelating agents in addition to their other properties. Especially effective chelating agents, such as ethylenediaminetetraacetic acid (EDTA, "versene"), bring about considerable changes in plant metabolism, probably by affecting processes involving metals.

When EDTA is added in sufficient quantity to a mineral medium supporting good growth, it profoundly modifies the photoperiodic responses of a clone of *Lemna perpusilla* and a clone of *Lemna gibba*. *Lemna perpusilla*, previously daylength-indifferent, now responds as a typical SDP; *Lemna gibba*, unable to flower under any photoperiod on the first medium, now flowers rapidly as an LDP in the medium with EDTA. The effects of EDTA on vegetative growth are quite minor and not related to photoperiod. It seems obvious that the major effect of EDTA here is not directly on flowering itself but on flowering through its sensitivity to photoperiod, since in *Lemna perpusilla* EDTA permits a long-day inhibition of flowering whereas in *Lemna gibba* it permits a long-day promotion. These effects are related to a report by Kandeler (1955) —the first in which the control of flowering in any duckweed was observed—that *Lemna gibba* flowered under long photoperiods given with fluorescent light only in "aged" medium, in which the plants had grown for some time. It now appears that EDTA substitutes for this "aged" medium effect and vice versa. Since, at least in *Lemna perpusilla*, chelating agents other than EDTA are effective, the action is not specific to EDTA alone and is probably a consequence of chelation (Hillman, 1959a, 1959b, 1961a, 1961b).

It has recently appeared that in more purified media, these two plants show their photoperiodic responses even in the absence of EDTA. Under these conditions, very low levels of cupric or mercuric ions promote *Lemna perpusilla* flowering in long days, have no effect in short days, and inhibit *Lemna gibba* flowering in long days. Thus these ions, by the reasoning above, appear to be relatively specific inhibitors of the response to long days; the action of the chelating agents observed earlier probably represents prevention of the effects of contaminants (undoubtedly copper) in the medium. Such results may provide new tools for the analysis of photoperiodism; however, much further work will be required to explore such a complex and sensitive experimental system (Hillman, 1961c).

chapter seven ❯ Age and Flowering

In the growth of most plants from seed, an appreciable period elapses before flowers are initiated even under conditions that would cause rapid flowering in more mature individuals. This is often expressed by saying that in order to flower a plant must reach the stage of readiness or "ripeness-to-flower," the latter being a rendering of Klebs's (1918) term *Blühreife*. Put so abstractly the concept seems merely circular, but it is not unique in this regard. Dormancy often seems to be defined as a state in which growth does not take place under conditions favorable in all respects—except for that condition required to break "dormancy." However, this merely illustrates the limitation of abstract statements since the questions involved in both dormancy and ripeness-to-flower are quite real.

The relationship of age or developmental stage to the ability to flower is not well understood, and differs vastly from species to species. The requirement for a considerable amount of vegetative growth is particularly marked in woody plants; many trees do not flower until at least ten years of age, and some "juvenile" phases are characterized not only by inability to flower but also by growth habits and leaf shapes differing from those of the adult phase (see Sax, 1958a). In herbaceous species, similar events lasting a much shorter time are often observed.

Since plants differ so greatly in the speed with which they become ripe-to-flower, and probably in the mechanism involved, the concept itself has little use except to call attention to a whole range of phenomena. In spite of this, an even more general concept,

116

that of "phasic development," has been associated with some studies. It views plant growth as a succession of recognizable phases, each requiring a specific set of environmental conditions for its fulfillment, and none of which can be bypassed (see Murneek and Whyte, 1948). A concept as unspecific as this is hardly susceptible either to proof or disproof once it is admitted that the characteristics of the phases will not be the same in all plants. Hence, it will not be considered further. Instead, some relationships of age and flowering in some of the familiar herbaceous plants will be discussed first, and will be followed by a consideration of the problems posed by flowering in woody species.

AGE AND FLOWERING IN HERBACEOUS PLANTS

Certain plants produce a characteristic minimum leaf number before flower primordia are initiated. In the best-known examples, spring and vernalized winter rye, a minimum of seven leaves appear before the inflorescences no matter what the conditions used, at least in most of the older research with these plants. A partial explanation is that four leaf primordia are already present in the mature embryo, and so precede the inflorescence. However, three more are apparently differentiated during or after germination. Although it is possible to reduce the "minimum leaf number" below 6 by the use of continuous light from germination, or by starting with prematurely harvested embryos that have differentiated fewer leaf primordia, apparently at least one or two leaves in addition to those in the embryo still intervene before flower initiation (Gott et al., 1955).

Holdsworth (1956) has considered the concept of minimum leaf number extensively, and questions its general usefulness. The number in Xanthium—8—appears to be accounted for by those leaves present in the embryo plus those developing before induction and the translocation of the floral stimulus have taken place. In certain other plants the number is higher than can be accounted for in such ways. However, both types of observation may depend on differences in the sensitivity of successive leaves to photoperiodic induction, which will be considered below. Other factors affecting minimum leaf number may be the movement of flower-inhibiting or promoting substances from the cotyledons, as observed, for example, in grafting experiments by Paton and Barber (1955) and Haupt (1958) on early and late flowering in peas (see Chapter Five). There are also plants in which the flower primordia, following a certain number of leaves, are already present in the seed (see Naylor, 1953).

One should attempt to distinguish between minimum leaf number, as in the case above, representing a condition in which a certain amount of development takes place before and during the treatments leading to flowering, and ripeness-to-flower understood as a condition before which a given treatment is completely ineffective in promoting flowering. In practice, such distinctions may be difficult to make. If the treatment in question is vernalization, however, it is clear that the difference between winter annuals and biennials (Chapter Five) simply reflects the fact that the latter are not responsive until they have attained a considerable size. In this sense, some winter annuals are ripe-to-flower as germinating seeds. The reason for the size requirement in biennials is not known, and has been ascribed to many factors, including the amount of food reserves. De Zeeuw and Leopold (1955) found that the age at which seedlings of Brussels sprouts, *Brassica oleracea gemmifera,* a biennial, could be vernalized was decreased if the synthetic auxin NAA was given together with the cold treatment; the effect was not great, so that evidence that the size requirement in biennials is related to auxin content is scanty.

A series of experiments by Sarkar (1958) on a winter-annual strain of the crucifer *Arabidopsis thaliana* illustrates not only the complexity of possible relationships between development and receptivity to cold treatment, but also the fact that the cold treatment itself may have a multiple action, as evidenced by the ability of gibberellin to replace it at some stages but not at others. The strain of *Arabidopsis* in question is easily vernalizable in the seed, during germination, or in the mature rosette stage. Young rosettes are less easily vernalized. Gibberellic acid, however, is most effective on the young rosettes, less so on the older, and totally ineffective on seeds.

Many studies bearing on ripeness-to-flower deal with responsiveness to photoperiod. In certain plants, of course, previous vernalization is a major factor affecting such responsiveness and thus also ripeness-to-flower in this sense. Since this relationship was discussed earlier, the discussion below will be concerned primarily with other prerequisites for the photoperiodic control of flowering.

Klebs (1918) originated this field of inquiry by observing that *Sempervivum funkii* did not show a flowering response to long days until it had been growing for some time, and he concluded that the best conditions to bring about this *Blühreife* state were those involving a high degree of carbon dioxide assimilation and a relatively meager mineral nutrition. This, as well as other observations by Klebs, was in part the origin of investigations on the C/N ratio (Chapter Six). It seems clear now that for most photoperiodic plants, probably including *Sempervivum,* gross nutrition is less important than the morphological stage of development attained.

Certain plants do not respond to an inductive photoperiod until they have produced true leaves, but there are some in which the cotyledons themselves are sensitive. These include the SDP *Pharbitis* (Nakayama, 1958) and *Chenopodium rubrum,* some strains of which may flower as tiny seedlings barely emerged from the seed coat (Cumming, 1959; see illustration facing page 1). The SDP *Xanthium* and *Perilla,* on the other hand, are of the former type. The development of at least one true leaf is necessary before *Xanthium* can respond to short days. Jennings and Zuck (1954), testing the possibility that this might be due to insufficient area of the expanded cotyledons, found that an area of true leaf considerably smaller than the total cotyledon area could induce flowering.

In *Perilla,* the sensitivity to induction of successive pairs of leaves increases from the second to at least the fifth pair, with the first and second being almost insensitive. This again does not appear to be a matter of leaf area or even of plant size, but represents a developmental difference in the leaves. For example, if equal areas (see Fig. 5-3, p. 86) are cut from second and fifth leaves, grafted onto other plants in long day, and then induced with short-day treatments so that they will function as donors, the tissue from the fifth leaves is by far more effective. However, the fact that intact older plants respond more quickly than younger plants is also due to greater total leaf area (Zeevaart, 1958). In the grass *Lolium temulentum,* the increasing sensitivity of the entire plant to photoperiod is attributable entirely to the increasing sensitivity of successively produced leaves. When only several lower leaves are left on a mature plant, as many long days are required to induce as are required by a much younger plant. However, a small portion of the area of one later-produced leaf is sufficient for induction by one long day (Evans, 1960).

The change in sensitivity of successive leaves, as in *Perilla*, may be a function of meristem aging. It is also possible that as the meristem itself ages, it becomes more sensitive to the floral stimulus from other parts of the plant; the general question of meristem aging and flowering may also be important for flowering in woody plants (see below) but little is known about it.

At least in *Xanthium*, the photoperiodic sensitivity of each leaf varies during its development. Khudairi and Hamner (1954a) studied the flowering responses of plants in which single leaves of different ages and at different stages in expansion were present. Within a wide range of absolute sizes, leaves were most sensitive when they had expanded to about half their final size, being much less so either when very young or when mature. Undoubtedly similar relationships between individual leaf development and photoperiodic sensitivity obtain in other plants as well.

It is not always true that photoperiodic sensitivity increases with plant age or development. The opposite situation has already been noted in sunflower (Chapter Two). It is an SDP when young but later becomes daylength-indifferent (Dyer *et al.*, 1959); stated otherwise, long days inhibit flowering in the young plant but not in the older. On the other hand, this can still be regarded as an increased sensitivity in the sense that a shorter nightlength is inductive in older plants. The mechanism is unknown.

FLOWERING IN WOODY PLANTS

It is in the woody plants that the problem of ripeness-to-flower is most obvious. The two major environmental factors affecting flowering in herbaceous plants—photoperiod and temperature—also of course affect woody plants, and by similar mechanisms; however, the dominant factor here, that of maturity, appears to be internal. The lack of flowering in many trees until they have attained a given age is of great practical importance because it affects both food production and breeding programs, and also makes experiments slow and costly. Hence the effectiveness of some of the procedures traditionally used in the hope of hastening flowering has only recently been confirmed in controlled experiments, and the value of some others is still uncertain.

Further problems are presented by the fact that most trees and shrubs, at least in the temperate zone, are probably indirect-flowering plants unlike most herbs studied, so that conditions required for flower initiation may differ greatly from those favoring flower development, and the internal changes involved may differ as well. As an extreme example, the difficulties faced by the forest geneticist are evident in the fact that not only must most species of pine (*Pinus*) grow for some five or more years before flower initiation is possible, but then two and a half years are required to obtain seed. Flower primordia are formed in the spring of one year but do not develop further until the spring of the next, when pollination takes place. Then in the succeeding spring and summer cone elongation and actual fertilization finally occur, following which the seeds mature in the fall (see Stanley, 1958). Clearly, any way of reducing the age required for flowering and speeding up the reproductive cycle itself would be extremely helpful.

A particular group of woody plants, the bamboos (Tribe Bambuseae of the grass family), provides the most striking examples of long-lived monocarpic plants (Chapter One), which flower once and then die. As summarized by Arber (1934), there is abundant evidence that a bamboo will spend 5 to 50 years, the number being characteristic of the species, in vigorous vegetative growth. It then flowers, sets seed, and dies within a short time. Usually all plants of the species within a large area will flower at the same time, regardless of injury or even of destruction of all portions above ground by cutting or fire. Thus size alone does not appear to be a factor. Individuals transplanted to, say, the Kew Botanical Gardens still flower the same year as their fellows in the tropics, making it seem unlikely that periodic environmental changes such as droughts are the cause of such behavior—although this has been suggested. Possibly bamboos may provide instances of very long-term endogenous rhythms, but it will take a long-lived plant physiologist or a well-endowed research institute to find out. Certainly in no group of plants is the relation between age and flowering more evident and less understood.

Most environmental factors affecting flowering in trees have been studied relatively little because of the obvious technical difficulties. Increased soil fertility may be of value (for experiments that deal with this possibility using pine, see Hoekstra and Mergen, 1957). Fraser (1958) has correlated meteorological data with anatomical studies of spruce (*Picea*), and concluded that earlier reports that flower initiation is favored by high summer temperatures are probably correct. Reference to the discussions in the papers cited will indicate that, unfortunately, tree physiologists are generally uncertain about the importance of any particular soil or climatic factor.

Photoperiodism affects largely the vegetative development of woody plants rather than flowering, at least according to present evidence. The rate of growth, its cessation and renewal, branching habit, leaf shape, and resistance to cold are among the characteristics affected (see Wareing, 1956; Nitsch, 1957). Such characteristics are often of great ecological significance, and their sensitivity to photoperiod frequently differs considerably within offspring of the same species gathered over a wide geographical area (see Vaartaja, 1959). In certain crop trees, such as the SDP *Coffea arabica* (coffee), flowering also is photoperiodically controlled (Piringer and Borthwick, 1955), whereas the ornamental shrub *Cestrum nocturnum* has been previously discussed as an LSDP.

Most work with economically important trees, however, suggests a minor role or none at all for photoperiodism in flower initiation. This is almost certainly true for pines (Mirov, 1956; see Mirov and Stanley, 1959), for peaches (*Prunus*), and probably for apples (*Malus*) (Piringer and Downs, 1959). One should note an indication of control by light in the last-named tree, however. In the paper cited, the variety used failed to flower at all on 16-hour photoperiods of which 8 hours were under fluorescent light, but flowered well if incandescent light was used. For such reasons, as well as because of the relatively few experiments done so far, it is impossible to guess whether or not photoperiodically controlled flowering is truly less common among woody plants than it appears to be among herbs. Certainly, however, even when photoperiodism is a direct factor, that of size or maturity is still of overriding interest both practically and theoretically.

Because of effects on vegetative growth, photoperiodic treatment can indirectly hasten flowering. A species of birch, *Betula verrucosa,* normally requiring at least 5 years from seed in order to flower, was used by Longman and Wareing (1959) in a study on whether size was the major factor involved or whether a certain number of developmental seasonal "cycles" were necessary before flowering could take place. Some seedlings were kept constantly under long days or continuous light, in which vegetative growth continues rapidly. Others were allowed to make about 30 centimeters of growth under such conditions, given short days to induce dormancy, and then kept in the cold for six weeks, following which they were returned to long days and the cycle repeated. There was also a control series under natural conditions. Fifty percent of the trees in the constant long-day conditions flowered within the first year, when 2 to 3 meters high, whereas none of the (smaller) control or "cycle" series flowered within two years. Hence in this tree at least, attainment of a certain size is crucial to flowering and can be speeded by constant long photoperiods, although the authors noted that the plants so treated were abnormally spindly.

Although flowering may thus be hastened by speeding development to the requisite size, most of the traditional methods used by horticulturists involve operations or mutilations of some kind and bring about an inhibition of vegetative growth. Of these methods, one of the most widely favored is girdling—the removal of a ring of bark, including phloem, on an entire tree or on a branch. The immediate result is to prevent the translocation of photosynthate out of the girdled top or branch, so that materials accumulate above the girdle. Naturally, this can thus result in the death by starvation of the root system if it is not permitted to heal over within a relatively short time. Girdling is often effective in causing flowering of plants too young to flower otherwise in species as unrelated as *Citrus* (Furr *et al.,* 1947), *Pinus* (Hoekstra and Mergen, 1957), and apples (Sax, 1957, 1958b). Related to girdling as a means of blocking phloem translocation is the technique of bark inversion, in which a ring of bark is cut out and regrafted in place upside down. Such procedures must be used before the period in which flower initiation would normally be expected to take place. In apples, bark inversion in June will affect flowering the following spring, even bringing it about in 2- or 3-year-old seedlings, whereas the same operation in late summer is ineffective (Sax, 1957, 1958b).

With many fruit trees, grafting young scions onto dwarfing stocks is another method whereby both a promotion of flowering and an inhibition of growth are obtained. The stocks are usually varieties of the same or a closely related species, and may be used either as rootstocks or interstocks. The latter method involves first grafting the dwarfing stock onto a standard seedling rootstock and later grafting the variety to be dwarfed onto the developed dwarfing tissue, so that the latter is interposed between root and crown. The mechanism by which such procedures cause early flowering is not known, but may in some cases be related to the reduction of phloem transport out of the scions and thus analogous to girdling. However, the interactions between stock and scion in such grafts are often highly specific, and not all grafts that reduce growth or transport promote flowering. In addition, not all grafts that cause early flowering and dwarfing appear to involve inhibited phloem transport (Sax, 1958b).

Another traditional method of handling fruit trees, the espalier technique, in which branches are bent horizontally or downward out of their normal direction, suggests that orientation with respect to gravity may affect flower initiation. This supposition was directly tested with young plants of several kinds of fruit trees by Wareing and Nasr (1958), who found marked effects on apples. Nineteen young shoots held in a horizontal position initiated a total of 116 flower buds in contrast to a control series initiating 5. Smaller but similar effects were observed in cherries (*Prunus*). Similar results have also been obtained by Longman and Wareing (1958) on young Japanese larch (*Larix*) trees. These are all, of course, reminiscent of results with pineapple and soybeans that may involve a changed auxin distribution, and it has also been suggested that the flower-promoting effects of bark inversion may be due to effects on auxin distribution, which then affect phloem transport (Sax, 1958b).

As repeatedly noted, most of the methods described above have in common either a demonstrated or possible effect of causing the accumulation of photosynthate near the growing points affected. The promotion of flower initiation in some trees by the early removal of fruits might also be attributed to an increase in available carbohydrates (for experiments of this kind dealing with *Citrus*, see Furr and Armstrong, 1956). The general hypothesis that maturity, and hence flowering, in many trees depends on a high level of carbohydrates is by no means unequivocally supported by the evidence at present, but it is attractive in view of Wetmore's (1953) observations, discussed in Chapter Five, that juvenility and maturity in fern leaf forms, and hence in the apex producing them, are clearly correlated to sucrose supply. On the other hand, more specific mechanisms of a hormonal nature may be involved in the flowering of trees.

In view of the work with herbaceous plants leading to the florigen hypothesis, it is surprising how few experiments have been published on the flowering responses of young scions after grafting to mature, flowering plants. Sax (1958a) indicates that this technique is common among tree breeders, but that there is no conclusive evidence for its effectiveness. Furr *et al.* (1947) found it completely ineffective in *Citrus.* In this connection, results of the opposite kind of graft are also of interest. Freely flowering branches from mature trees have been grafted on young stocks in order to facilitate seed collection. Although Huber (1952) reports this technique as successful in poplar (*Populus*), there are cases in which mature scions on young stocks revert to a nonflowering condition after several years (see Fraser, 1958). Whether this reflects an insufficient supply of flower-promoting factors (florigen, carbohydrates) from stock to scion, or the movement of inhibitors, or some other relationship, is not known.

The entire problem of juvenility is obviously closely related to the subject matter of this chapter. It is particularly relevant with regard to woody plants, but also probably important in herbs. This problem has attracted relatively little attention in recent years, but the interested reader should consult Sinnott (1960) for a consideration of the literature. One striking if somewhat atypical example, related to flowering, is provided by ivy (*Hedera*). The young plant is a vine, with lobed leaves and aerial roots. After 10 or 12 years it produces branches that grow upward, bearing entire leaves and no aerial roots. Only these branches are capable of flowering. If they are cut off and rooted they grow into erect shrubs that may become very large and rarely if ever revert to the juvenile vine condition, although shoots produced from the base of old shrub (or arborescent) forms may be juvenile—a phenomenon observed also in apple and other trees with distinct juvenile forms (see Sax, 1958a). Recent work by Robbins (1957, 1960) has shown that reversion will occur after either heavy pruning or treatment with gibberellic acid, and also that it is possible to obtain forms intermediate between typically adult and typically juvenile. Gibberellic acid also causes the production of vegetative inflorescences. However, the factors governing the attainment of the adult state in the first place are entirely unknown, and further work with this sort of organism should be valuable for an understanding of both flowering and differentiation in general.

chapter eight

❯❯❯❯❯❯ A Miscellany

Several topics that have escaped the more systematic treatment in preceding chapters will be considered briefly in this one. The brevity does not imply that these topics are unimportant, but is a product of space limitations and the fact that this book, like most of the recent literature, is concerned with the circumstances bringing about flowering rather than with associated matters. In addition to the topics below, others connected with the physiology of flowering suggest themselves, notably the physiology of meiosis and of fertilization. These will be omitted entirely since an adequate consideration would require a general discussion of the physiology of reproduction, taking in material far beyond the scope of this survey. A few remarks on the future of the physiology of flowering conclude both chapter and book.

ANTHESIS

The culminating stage in flower development is the opening of the bud, anthesis, with which is often associated the attainment of the flower's characteristic color and scent. Most of the work on anthesis has been concerned with the precise diurnal timing often shown by this event. In the literature on endogenous rhythms, anthesis is considered as one of the many phenomena under such control. The effects of light and darkness on a number of plants support this view.

Among the earlier studies, perhaps the most interesting are two papers by N. G. Ball on several plants whose flowers normally open early in the morning. For example, those of the tropical perennial herb, *Turnera ulmifolia,* open about two hours after dawn, then wither three or four hours later. This occurs in successive groups of buds even if the shoots are kept in darkness for several days so that they are isolated from the normal day-night changes. However, it is possible to prevent opening by illumination during the night, particularly during the second half of the night, and the anthesis-inhibiting effect of one such illumination lasts for the next three days. Air temperature and relative humidity changes appear to have little effect (Ball, 1933).

Ball (1936) found similar inhibiting effects of night illumination on morning anthesis in species of *Campanula, Geranium, Cistus,* and *Ipomoea.* He determined a crude action spectrum for this phenomenon, using filters, and found that red (6500–7000 Å) was the most effective and blue the least effective color. With the advantage of twenty-five years, it is easy to interpret these results as representing the disturbance of a circadian rhythm originally "set" by the light-dark schedule through what is presumably the red, far-red system. However, this work was in a sense before its time, so the (for then) unusual effectiveness of red light attracted little attention.

A paper by Arnold (1959) on *Oenothera* (evening primrose) indicates that endogenous rhythms are also involved here, though relatively susceptible to modification. If the plants receive light from 6 A.M. to 6 P.M. the flowers open at about 6 P.M., as in nature; with an inverse cycle, they open in the morning. Anthesis of a bud that is ready occurs roughly 12 hours after a dark-to-light transition, which thus appears to "set" the timing mechanism, but the timer is easily perturbed by the length of the light period itself. On a schedule of 18 hours light-6 hours darkness anthesis is regularly later, and on 6 hours light-18 hours darkness regularly earlier, than would be predicted by the 12-hour rule. However, it is clear that there is an endogenous component to the timing since anthesis will not follow any arbitrary cycle of light and darkness. The circadian periodicity of anthesis cannot be made into a 12-hour periodicity by schedules of 6 hours light-6 hours darkness, nor into a 48-hour periodicity by alternating 24-hour light and dark periods.

According to Arnold's investigations the light-sensitive timer of *Oenothera* anthesis must be localized in the buds. In continuous darkness, anthesis occurs with circadian periodicity for several days, but only in those buds that had developed largely under normal day-night changes. Buds that develop from a young stage in total darkness are considerably delayed in anthesis, and finally open more or less at random. In addition, light must be given directly to the buds to reset or disturb the periodicity of anthesis—lighting schedules given to the leaves are ineffective.

Other evening-blooming plants have been studied recently. Anthesis of the giant tropical water lily *Victoria regia* normally occurs soon after sunset (6 p.m.). It can be moved up as early as 4 p.m. by darkening the buds with black paper for 30 minutes, but darkening earlier than this hour has no effect; therefore some endogenous component, perhaps set by preceding illumination schedules, is involved in the sensitivity to darkness. Illumination during the night delays the opening of buds during the next days, but eventually they open even in continuous light (Gessner, 1960). The opening and odor production of the night-blooming jasmine, *Cestrum nocturnum* (an LSDP discussed earlier), show a circadian rhythm in constant light or darkness. In constant light, the period length is roughly 27 hours at 17° C; higher temperatures reduce it by several hours, and lower temperatures increase it (Overland, 1960).

Daily timing of anthesis is probably regulated in the ways indicated above, but much less is known about the control of anthesis in those indirect-flowering plants whose fully developed buds may remain dormant for a considerable period and then open in the course of a few days. Among temperate-zone plants this is usually the result of the breaking of dormancy by long cold exposure followed by periods of favorable temperatures for growth; as such, it resembles the breaking of other forms of dormancy by low temperature (see Chouard, 1960). Though this does not explain it, there is no need for further consideration as a separate topic here. Certain tropical plants, however, show the same extended bud dormancy, and the same explanation cannot hold for these.

One of the few examples studied with any thoroughness is coffee, *Coffea arabica*. This is an SDP as far as flower initiation is concerned (Chapter Seven), but bud dormancy and anthesis appear to be controlled by moisture conditions. Under relatively dry conditions, rapid and uniform anthesis can be brought on by heavy rains or irrigation—even by wetting the buds themselves. This suggests that the seasonal dormancy is simply due to a water deficit and disappears when water is supplied. But the situation is probably not this simple. Alvim (1960), working in a dry area where the water conditions on a plantation were completely controllable by irrigation, found that coffee plants irrigated at weekly intervals failed to reach anthesis over a long period of time. Others, allowed to remain dry for a shorter length of time and then given one good irrigation, responded with heavy anthesis within two weeks. It thus seems likely that a period of water deficit is required to break bud dormancy in this plant, so that anthesis is brought about by a thorough wetting *after* a dry period. Alvim suggests that this may be a major form of seasonal control of anthesis in tropical plants, a control in some respects ecologically analogous to that exerted in temperate-zone plants by low temperatures followed by warming.

THE SEX EXPRESSION OF FLOWERS

Flower primordia in a given species do not always give rise to identical structures, even if development is perfectly normal. Although probably the great majority of plants produce one kind of flower, with both functional stamens and functional pistils—a hermaphrodite or monoclinous flower—some do not. Unisexual (or diclinous) flowers, either staminate or pistillate, occur in many species. There are also intermediate conditions of various kinds. If staminate and pistillate flowers are borne on the same individual, the plant is said to be monoecious; if on separate individuals, dioecious. Until relatively recently, these phenomena of "sex expression" have been studied largely from the morphological and genetic points of view, but they are frequently modifiable by environmental and chemical means as well. For a recent review of the genetic factors, see Westergaard (1958). A comprehensive review by Heslop-Harrison (1957) on the experimental modification of sex expression is the basis for the general statements not otherwise documented in the discussion below. There are some controversy over the evolutionary origins of sex expression in plants and even over the proper terms in which to discuss it (see the references cited and also Heslop-Harrison, 1958).

Consideration of the effects of light and temperature on sex expression might best begin with a study by Nitsch *et al.* (1952) on a monoecious plant, the acorn squash (a variety of *Cucurbita pepo*). This plant produces one flower primordium at each node, and the primordia develop differently depending on their position in the sequence of nodes. The earliest give rise to underdeveloped staminate ("male") flowers; these are followed by normal staminate flowers that are followed in turn by normal pistillate ("female") flowers; interspersed among the nodes bearing the latter are nodes with inhibited staminate flowers. Still later, giant pistillate flowers occur, again interspersed with inhibited staminates; finally even larger pistillate flowers are produced that are parthenocarpic, producing fruits (but not seeds) without pollination. This trend of "feminization" occurs under all conditions, but the duration of each phase in terms of node number is easily modified. High temperatures and long days delay it, favoring the continued production of staminate flowers, whereas low temperatures and short days speed feminization greatly. Either daylength or temperature can be made the dominating factor depending on the values used. The control exerted is striking: for example, female flowers can be made to appear as early as the ninth, or as late as the hundredth node.

It is not clear whether the effects referred to daylength are photoperiodic in the strict sense. Supplementary light of 1000 foot candles was used, and no low-intensity interruptions attempted. One observation in the paper suggests that lower intensities might not be as effective. In addition, some conclusions on the greater effectiveness of "night" than of "day" temperatures are weakened by the fact that the former were always given for 16 hours daily, the latter for only the 8 hours of daily sunlight employed, in each treatment, irrespective of supplementary light schedules. These points do not detract from the dramatic climatic effects reported, but the paper is chief among those usually cited as indicating control of sex expression by "photoperiod" and "thermoperiodicity," interpretations that may be overstated.

Most other investigations with temperature, on both monoecious and dioecious plants, agree with the results described in showing low temperatures favoring pistillate development and high favoring staminate. The effects of daylength, whether strictly photoperiodic or not, are more complex. Apparently the generalization holds that pistillate flowers represent a fuller intensity of flowering than staminate flowers; thus, with photoperiodic plants, prolonged short-day treatment favors pistillate expression relative to staminate in SDP, whereas long-day treatment does so in LDP. For example, in the LDP spinach, normally dioecious, short days following long-day induction cause the formation of some staminate flowers on plants that would normally produce only the pistillate, thus making the treated plants monoecious (see Heslop-Harrison, 1957).

The factors that affect sex expression in plants with diclinous flowers may affect even plants with hermaphrodite flowers in a similar fashion. One particularly interesting example, dealing with the effect of photoperiod, has recently been studied by J. and Y. Heslop-Harrison (1958a,b). The plant is *Silene pendula,* an LDP in that flowering does not occur with 8 hours of daylight but is brought about by supplementing this to 21 hours with light of about 300 foot candles. Plants raised from germination on long days showed high male sterility, some 50 percent of the anthers being sterile; in addition, pistil development was excessive. Plants that had received some short-day exposure before being returned to long days, however, showed normal pistil development and fully fertile anthers. Hence this plant, while grossly an LDP in terms of mere flower initiation, is clearly an SLDP for normal flower development.

Chemical control of sex expression has been studied in a variety of plants. The earliest clear-cut results with auxins (chiefly naphthaleneacetic acid) were obtained on monoecious cucurbits such as the cucumber, *Cucumis sativus,* in which feminization is promoted (see, for example, Laibach and Kribben, 1950). Subsequent work on other plants as well seems to bear out the generalization that high auxin levels favor pistillate and reduce staminate expression. As with other factors, such effects are not confined to plants with unisexual flowers. The *Silene* work discussed above also included studies of the effects of auxin application; these, like continual exposure to long days, caused male sterility and overdevelopment of the pistil.

Other growth-regulating substances whose mechanism of action may be related to that of auxins also affect sex expression. Maleic hydrazide and 2,3,5-triiodobenzoic acid both may cause male sterility and otherwise suppress anther development, but often only in conjunction with other strong morphogenetic effects. A feminizing effect of carbon monoxide has been observed by J. and Y. Heslop-Harrison (1957) in a monoecious race of *Mercurialis*. This was accompanied by formative effects resembling those caused by auxins.

Three other chemical effects should be mentioned. High nitrogen levels generally promote pistillate as opposed to staminate expression; this has been observed on monoecious species and on at least one hermaphrodite, the tomato. The question of whether mammalian sex hormones may affect sex expression in higher plants has attracted surprisingly little attention. A single major investigation (Löve and Löve, 1945) with *Melandrium* showed highly significant effects in spite of high toxicity. Although similar work on a few other plants has found nothing of interest, the problem may still be worth pursuing.

The gibberellins have so far been little studied with regard to these phenomena, but may prove to be of great importance. Galun (1959) has found that gibberellic acid, unlike auxin, causes a trend toward "maleness"—prolonged staminate and delayed pistillate expression—in the cucumber; this effect is partially counteracted by naphthaleneacetic acid. Moreover, certain cucumber strains that normally produce only pistillate flowers will produce staminate flowers as well following gibberellic acid treatment. Besides its theoretical interest, this result also holds promise for practical breeding work (Peterson and Anhder, 1960).

So far, the only important hypothesis on the control of sex expression is that derived primarily from work with applied auxin; it envisages auxin level in the plant as the major controlling factor. Daylength, temperature, and other factors are considered to act through their effects on auxin level. Probably the most detailed statement is given by Heslop-Harrison (1957). In essence, optimum auxin levels for flowering are considered to be lower than those for vegetative growth; within the flowering range, the optimum for staminate expression is lower than that for pistillate expression. In a sense this hypothesis contradicts the suggestion, noted earlier, that the pistillate expression represents a more intense flowering condition than the staminate. As a working hypothesis, however, it has proved fruitful. Experiments on the relationships between flowering, sex expression, and leaf form, for example in hemp, *Cannabis sativa* (J. and Y. Heslop-Harrison, 1958c), have provided further evidence in its favor. Work of this sort also has implications for the questions of juvenility and maturity mentioned in the preceding chapter, but cannot be discussed in detail here. In addition, further information on the roles of other growth substances, notably the gibberellins, will certainly be required before a truly comprehensive hypothesis can be framed.

GENETICS OF FLOWERING RESPONSES

Flowering responses to photoperiod and temperature are of course genetically controlled, and from the relative ease with which "early" and "late" varieties of cultivated plants are bred, one might guess that this control is often quite simple. Although practical breeding work is not done with reference to narrowly defined physiological responses, a number of specific investigations confirm this guess.

The SDP characteristic of Maryland Mammoth tobacco has been studied in crosses with *Nicotiana tabacum* var. Java. The F_1 generation is not homogeneous, suggesting that the dominance of Java's day-neutral (or, more accurately, weakly quantitative LDP) characteristic is incomplete. In the F_2, however, the SDP character occurs in approximately one-fourth of the progeny, indicating dependence on a single recessive gene. The "mammoth" (essentially SDP) character apparently occurs frequently in various tobacco varieties as a single-gene mutation, but its expression is affected by other genetic properties of the variety. In the interspecific cross of Maryland Mammoth with the LDP *Nicotiana sylvestris,* the LDP character is completely dominant (Lang, 1948). In similar crosses between the SDP *Coleus frederici* and the quantitative LDP *Coleus blumei* the F_1 plants are entirely SDP, indicating dominance of this characteristic (Kribben, 1955).

The difference between winter and spring varieties of Petkus rye appears to be due to a single gene. In the F_1 generation of a cross, the spring (noncold-requiring) habit is dominant; the F_2 generation segregates in a spring:winter ratio of 3:1. However, the dispersion in flowering time within the spring and winter classes of the F_2 indicates that the situation may not be quite as simple as the gross segregation suggests (Purvis, 1939). Sarkar (1958) has confirmed and extended earlier work on the cold requirement in *Hyoscyamus niger*. Here again, crosses between the annual and biennial strains indicate a single-gene difference in this regard, but there is no dominance. The F_1 is intermediate between homozygous annuals and homozygous biennials. The heterozygote will eventually respond to long days without a previous cold treatment, but does so more rapidly with it; a given cold treatment has a greater effect on the heterozygote than on the pure biennial; and the former reaches a vernalizable stage earlier in development than the latter.

Not all vernalization requirements appear to depend on single genes. Napp-Zinn (1960) reports in one paper of a continuing study on *Arabidopsis thaliana* that the difference between summer and winter annual strains depends on at least two genes. In addition, the relation between developmental stage and susceptibility to vernalization is under further genetic control, which has not been completely analyzed.

This brief survey will be sufficient to suggest the nature of such investigations. Two general observations are worth making in this connection. In the first place, it seems evident even from the little that is known that specific requirements for flowering are not necessarily genetically deep-seated, but may be easily acquired or lost. Hence conclusions about the distribution—geographical or geological—of species and families on the basis of the present-day response characters of certain members (for example, Allard, 1948), although stimulating, should be entertained with the greatest caution. Second, and perhaps more important, there is clearly room for much more work on the genetic control of flowering requirements. Cold requirements, at least, are currently receiving considerable attention (see Napp-Zinn, 1960) but genetic studies are notably inconspicuous or absent in most of the recent literature on photoperiodism. The difficulties should not be underestimated—particularly those involved in finding SDP and LDP sufficiently closely related to allow crossing, a difficulty that in itself may be of great importance. However, with the increasingly precise knowledge that research in flowering may be expected to gain from investigations as diverse as those on the red, far-red system and with chemical controlling agents, a biochemical genetics of flowering as envisaged by Lang (1948) should be a perfectly attainable goal, and well worth the effort.

FLOWERING AND DEATH

In addition to providing a melodramatic heading, the relationship between these two processes is sufficiently intimate in some plants—the monocarpic—to warrant some further mention.

One reason for death following heavy flowering might be simply morphological. If all the shoot meristems are converted to determinate structures, vegetative growth cannot continue—at least without the formation of adventitious buds. Whether this complete conversion of all meristematic areas into flowers ever actually occurs is of course another question, but the possibility can be envisaged.

The usual explanation of death following flowering and fruiting is nutritional—death is seen as the result of metabolic patterns in which the flowers, fruits, and seeds in some way compete so successfully with the rest of the plant for energy sources and other materials that death is the eventual result. The evidence is largely from observations, so often made, that the life of annuals can be prolonged by removing flowers and young fruits. However, it has recently been pointed out that there may be other explanations for such results, such as the production of inhibitors at various stages of reproductive development. For example, senescence in staminate spinach plants can be put off for a long time by removing the flowers. Since no fruit or seed could be set by these plants under any circumstances, and the staminate flowers themselves do not appear to contain large amounts of reserves, the simple nutritional hypothesis seems very weak here (Leopold et al., 1959). The article cited contains additional experiments and references on this topic, which is largely unexplored.

It has already been mentioned many times that there are close relationships between flowering and vegetative growth habit, depending upon the plant; it is usually unclear whether a given growth change is directly related causally to flowering or whether both express another underlying condition. The relationship in monocarpic plants thus represents another, and surely the ultimate, aspect of this more general problem.

PROSPECTS

From time to time throughout this survey suggestions for future work have been briefly made. In an overall view, however, the directions of research in the physiology of flowering are hard to predict with any accuracy, and harder still to recommend with any assurance. The best thing may be simply to ruminate a little on the subject before going back to work.

One can see that most of the large problems remain. Indeed, one of the major achievements of the research of the past few decades was to delineate these questions in the first place. Among them are the nature or natures of the persistent states induced by photoperiodic or cold treatments; the nature of the flower-controlling substances that move between plant parts or between grafted plants; whether or not endogenous circadian rhythms constitute the basic mechanism of photoperiodism; and the relationships between juvenility, maturity, and flowering.

Some questions have been reduced to simpler forms. For example, a question on the role of light and darkness in photoperiodism can be reshaped, at least in part, much more sharply: What is the biochemical role of the red, far-red pigment? Some developmental questions—bolting in rosette plants, for instance—can now be asked, again at least in part, in terms of specific growth substances, the gibberellins. This increased concreteness obviously represents progress; and as long as the answers to such simpler questions are not mistaken for exhaustive explanations of all associated phenomena, they should increase that progress.

A major goal—perhaps the only goal—of physiology can be stated as the understanding of growth and development in terms of simpler biochemical systems and their integration. This does not mean that physiology is or ought to be biochemistry; in a sense, the biochemist's job begins where the physiologist's ends, although in practice they necessarily overlap immensely. One can envision the physiologist as taking an organism apart into relatively large portions—speaking in terms of processes—that are then susceptible to biochemical investigation. Unfortunately, the general recognition of the close relationship between physiology and biochemistry has occasionally led to almost meaningless work. For example, an enzyme or other substance is assayed in tissues at two quite different stages of development; a difference is found, and this biochemical difference is now suggested as the cause of the developmental difference, in spite of the fact that it may be, and probably is, merely a correlation. Such work may be quite interesting, biochemically speaking, but the physiologist must always keep in mind the need of a causal analysis. This at the very least requires attention to the kinetics—relations in time—of any two conditions, one of which is believed to cause the other. The physiology of flowering has had and will have its share of both sorts of biochemically oriented investigations, but probably only the kind of care with which Lang (1960) has started to analyze the relations between endogenous gibberellin level and bolting in *Hyoscyamus* will provide real understanding.

Assuming, then, the goal of taking organisms apart biochemically—as long as the "parts" so obtained fit together again, physiologically speaking—what other experimental approaches are available? A useful one in the past will continue to be so: the use of substances or conditions suspected of having relevant effects. Though easily mocked, in some forms, as "spray and weigh," this approach at least reduces the kinetics problem; the added substance or changed condition surely *precedes* the effect in a well-controlled experiment. However, the problem still remains of how directly the two are related. It is this kind of approach, in the broadest sense, that has led to the basic discoveries of photoperiodism and vernalization, as well as many others. Even genetic studies come into this general class.

Advantages can be gained here from the use of more convenient experimental materials. *Arabidopsis, Chenopodium* seedlings, and *Lemna* are all small enough to be grown rapidly in aseptic culture under highly controlled conditions, and may thus partially replace the unwieldy *Perilla* and *Xanthium* of classical investigations. However, the full exploitation of tissue culture techniques should make the latter materials even more useful than ever for studies of florigen and the induced state. For some preliminary thoughts and results in this particular direction, see Chailakhyan (1961) and Fox and Miller (1959).

An approach related to the two preceding has not been employed to any great extent. It involves following changes in both meristems and other tissues with the most sensitive cyto-chemical and other microscopic techniques. Ideally, this sort of work could provide suggestions as to what biochemical changes to investigate with grosser methods. Even relatively traditional ana-tomical studies can give important information on the action of various growth regulators (for example, Sachs *et al.,* 1959, 1960) and it would seem highly desirable to have such information as closely correlated as possible with that gained from other ap-proaches. Even some very simple-minded questions might have valuable answers: What are the differences, if any, in intracellular organization or content between induced and noninduced *Perilla* leaves, and how soon do they arise? During the time that florigen is believed to be moving from an induced leaf to a meristem, can changes be observed along its route? And so forth.

In short, the field will undoubtedly continue to progress as it has in the past—through critically tested guesses, appropriate choice of experimental material, perseverance, and technical advances. It is obvious by now that the writer has no revolutionary improve-ments in approach to propose, which is hardly surprising since differentiation and development have yielded their secrets slowly to better minds than his. But the progressive understanding of these problems, representing as they do much of what is contained in that simple word, "life," is surely an enterprise worthy of the best.

Bibliography

ALLARD, H. A., 1948. "Length of day in the climates of past geological eras and its possible effects upon changes in plant life," pp. 101–119 in A. E. Murneek and R. O. Whyte (eds.), *Vernalization and photoperiodism*, Waltham, Mass.: Chronica Botanica.

ALVIM, P. DE T., 1960. "Moisture stress as a requirement for flowering of coffee," *Science*, **132:** 354.

ARBER, A., 1934. *The gramineae. A study of cereals, bamboo and grass*, New York: Macmillan, xvii + 480 pp.

ARNOLD, C.-G., 1959. "Die Blütenöffnung bei *Oenothera* in Abhängigkeit vom Licht-dunkelrhythmus," *Planta*, **53:** 198–211.

AUDUS, L. J., 1959. *Plant growth substances*, 2d ed., New York: Interscience Publishers, xxii + 554 pp.

BALL, N. G., 1933. "A physiological investigation of the ephemeral flowers of *Turnera ulmifolia* L. var. *elegans* Urb." *New Phytol.*, **32:** 13–36.

———, 1936. "The effect of nocturnal illumination by different regions of the spectrum on the subsequent opening of flower-buds," *New Phytol.*, **35:** 101–116.

Biological clocks, 1960. Cold Spring Harbor Symposia on Quantitative Biology, XXV. Cold Spring Harbor, L. I., New York: Long Island Biological Association, xii + 524 pp.

BLANEY, L. T., and HAMNER, K. C., 1957. "Interrelations among effects of temperature, photoperiod, and dark period on floral initiation of Biloxi soybean," *Bot. Gaz.*, **119:** 10–24.

BONNER, J., 1949. "Further experiments on flowering in *Xanthium*," *Bot. Gaz.*, **110:** 625–627.

———, 1959a. "The photoperiodic process," pp. 245–254 in R. B. Withrow (ed.), *Photoperiodism and related phenomena in plants and animals*, Washington, D.C.: American Association for the Advancement of Science.

141

142 · BIBLIOGRAPHY

BONNER, J., 1959b. "Chemical nature of the inductive process," pp. 411–421 in R. B. Withrow (ed.), *Photoperiodism and related phenomena in plants and animals,* Washington, D.C.: American Association for the Advancement of Science.

———, and BONNER, D., 1948. "Notes on induction of flowering in *Xanthium,*" *Bot. Gaz.,* **110**: 154–156.

———, and LIVERMAN, J. L., 1953. "Hormonal control of flower initiation," pp. 283–304 in W. E. Loomis (ed.), *Growth and differentiation in plants,* Ames: Iowa State University Press.

———, and THURLOW, J., 1949. "Inhibition of photoperiodic induction in *Xanthium* by applied auxin," *Bot. Gaz.,* **110**: 613–624.

BORTHWICK, H. A., 1959. "Photoperiodic control of flowering," pp. 275–288 in R. B. Withrow (ed.), *Photoperiodism and related phenomena in plants and animals,* Washington, D.C.: American Association for the Advancement of Science.

———, and HENDRICKS, S. B., 1960. "Photoperiodism in plants," *Science,* **132**: 1223–1228.

———, ———, and PARKER, M. W., 1951. "Action spectrum for inhibition of stem growth in dark-grown seedlings of albino and nonalbino barley (*Hordeum vulgare*)," *Bot. Gaz.,* **110**: 103–118.

———, ———, ———, TOOLE, E. H., and TOOLE, V. K., 1952a. "A reversible photoreaction controlling seed germination," *Proc. Nat. Acad. Sci.,* **38**: 662–666.

———, ———, ———, 1952b. "The reaction controlling floral initiation," *Proc. Nat. Acad. Sci.,* **38**: 929–934.

———, ———, and PARKER, M. W., 1956. "Photoperiodism," pp. 479–517 in A. Hollaender (ed.), *Radiation biology,* Vol. III, New York: McGraw-Hill.

———, ———, TOOLE, E. H., and TOOLE, V. K., 1954. "Action of light on lettuce-seed germination," *Bot. Gaz.,* **115**: 205–225.

———, and PARKER, M. W., 1938a. "Influence of photoperiods upon the differentiation of meristems and the blossoming of Biloxi soybeans," *Bot. Gaz.,* **99**: 825–839.

———, ———, 1938b. "Photoperiodic perception in Biloxi soybeans," *Bot. Gaz.,* **100**: 374–387.

———, ———, and HEINZE, P. H., 1941. "Influence of localized low temperature on Biloxi soybean during photoperiodic induction," *Bot. Gaz.,* **102**: 792–800.

BRAUN, A. C., 1958. "A physiological basis for autonomous growth of the crown-gall tumor cell," *Proc. Nat. Acad. Sci.,* **44**: 344–349.

BRIAN, P. W., 1959. "Effects of gibberellins on plant growth and development," *Biol. Revs.,* **34**: 37–84.

BROWN, F. A., JR., 1959. "Living clocks," *Science,* **130**: 1535–1544.

BÜNNING, E., 1948. *Entwicklungs- und Bewegungsphysiologie der Pflanze,* Berlin, Göttingen, Heidelberg: Springer-Verlag, xii + 464 pp.

———, 1951. "Über Langtagpflanzen mit doppelter photophiler Phase," *Ber. Deutsch. Bot. Ges.,* **64**: 84–89.

———, 1954. "Der Verlauf der endogenen Tagesrhythmik bei photoperiodischen Störlicht-Versuchen mit *Soja,*" *Physiol. Plantarium,* **7**: 538–547.

BÜNNING, E., 1955. "Die Beziehung einiger photoperiodischer Phänomene bei *Soja* und *Xanthium* zur endogenen Tagesrhythmik," *Ber. Deutsch. Bot. Ges.,* 67: 421–431.

——, 1956. "Endogenous rhythms in plants," *Ann. Rev. Plant Physiol.,* 7: 71–90.

——, 1959a. "Physiological mechanism and biological importance of the endogenous diurnal periodicity in plants and animals," pp. 507–530 in R. B. Withrow (ed.), *Photoperiodism and related phenomena in plants and animals,* Washington, D.C.: American Association for the Advancement of Science.

——, 1959b. "Additional remarks on the role of the endogenous diurnal periodicity in photoperiodism," pp. 531–535 in R. B. Withrow (ed.), *Photoperiodism and related phenomena in plants and animals,* Washington, D.C.: American Association for the Advancement of Science.

——, 1959c. "Diurnal changes in pigment content and in the photoperiodic efficiency of red and far-red," pp. 537–540 in R. B. Withrow (ed.), *Photoperiodism and related phenomena in plants and animals,* Washington, D.C.: American Association for the Advancement of Science.

——, and KEMMLER, H., 1954. "Über den Phasenwechsel der endogenen Tagesrhythmik bei Langtagpflanzen," *Zeit. Bot.,* 42: 135–150.

BÜNSOW, R., PENNER, J., and HARDER, R., 1958. "Blütenbildung bei *Bryophyllum* durch Extrakt aus Bohnensamen," *Naturwiss.,* 45: 46–47.

BUTLER, W. L., NORRIS, K. H., SIEGELMAN, H. W., and HENDRICKS, S. B., 1959. "Detection, assay, and preliminary purification of the pigment controlling photoresponsive development of plants," *Proc. Nat. Acad. Sci.,* 45: 1703–1708.

BUVAT, R., 1955. "Le méristème apical de la Tige," *Ann. Biol.,* 59 (3ᵐᵉ Ser., T. 31): 595–656.

CARR, D. J., 1952. "A critical experiment on Bünning's theory of photoperiodism," *Zeit. Naturf.,* 7b: 570–571.

——, 1955. "On the nature of photoperiodic induction. III. The summation of the effects of inductive photoperiodic cycles," *Physiol. Plantarum,* 8: 512–526.

——, 1957. "On the nature of photoperiodic induction. IV. Preliminary experiments on the effect of light following the inductive long dark period in *Xanthium pennsylvanicum*," *Physiol. Plantarum,* 10: 249–265.

CASO, O. H., HIGHKIN, H. R., and KOLLER, D., 1960. "Effect of gibberellic acid on flower differentiation in Petkus winter rye," *Nature,* 185: 477–479.

CHAILAKHYAN, M. H., 1936a. "On the mechanism of photoperiodic reaction," *C. R. (Doklady) Acad. Sci. U.R.S.S.,* 10: 89–93.

——, 1936b. "On the hormonal theory of plant development," *C. R. (Doklady) Acad. Sci. U.R.S.S.,* 12: 443–447.

——, 1936c. "New facts in support of the hormonal theory of plant development," *C. R. (Doklady) Acad. Sci. U.R.S.S.,* 13: 79–83.

——, 1937. "Concerning the hormonal nature of plant development processes," *C. R. (Doklady) Acad. Sci. U.R.S.S.,* 16: 227–230.

CHAILAKHYAN, M. H., 1960. "Effect of gibberellins and derivatives of nucleic acid metabolism on plant growth and flowering," pp. 531–542 in *Plant growth regulation*, Ames: Iowa State University Press.

————, and ZHDANOVA, L. P., 1938. "Hormones of growth in formation processes. I. Photoperiodism and the reaction of growth hormones," *C. R. (Doklady) Acad. Sci. U.R.S.S.*, **19**: 107–111.

CHOUARD, P., 1957. "Quelques problèmes évoqués par la diversité des réactions des plantes à fleurs au photopériodisme," pp. 7–23 in *Colloque International sur le Photo-thermopériodisme*, Union Internationale des Sciences Biologiques, Série B (Colloques) No. 34. Rue Victor Cousin, Paris: Secrétariat de l'U.I.S.B. (Publications).

————, 1960. "Vernalization and dormancy," *Ann. Rev. Plant Physiol.*, **11**: 191–238.

CLAES, H., and LANG, A., 1947. "Die Blütenbildung von *Hyoscyamus niger* in 48-stündigen Licht-Dunkel-Zyklen und in Zyklen mit aufgeteilten Licht-phasen," *Zeit. Naturf.*, **2b**: 56–63.

CLAUSS, H., and RAU, W., 1956. "Uber die Blütenbildung von *Hyoscyamus niger* und *Arabidopsis thaliana* in 72-Studen-Zyklen," *Zeit. Bot.*, **44**: 437–454.

COOKE, A. R., 1954. "Changes in free auxin content during the photoinduction of short-day plants," *Plant Physiol.*, **29**: 440–444.

CORDNER, H. B., and HEDGES, G., 1959. "Determinateness in the tomato in relation to variety and to application of N-metatolylphthalamic acid of high concentration," *Proc. Am. Soc. Hort. Sci.*, **73**: 323–330.

CUMMING, B. G., 1959. "Extreme sensitivity of germination and photoperiodic reaction in the genus *Chenopodium* (Tourn.) L.," *Nature*, **184**: 1044–1045.

DE LINT, P. J. A. L., 1960. "An attempt to analysis of the effect of light on stem elongation and flowering in *Hyoscyamus niger* L.," *Med. Landbouwhogeschool Wageningen*, **60**: 1–59.

DE ZEEUW, D., 1953. "Flower initiation and light intensity in *Perilla*," *Koninkl. Ned. Akad., Wet., Proc.*, **C56**: 418–422.

————, and LEOPOLD, A. C., 1955. "Altering juvenility with auxin," *Science*, **122**: 925–926.

DOORENBOS, J., and WELLENSIEK, S. J., 1959. "Photoperiodic control of floral induction," *Ann. Rev. Plant Physiol.*, **10**: 147–184.

DOWNS, R. J., 1956. "Photoreversibility of flower initiation," *Plant Physiol.*, **31**: 279–284.

————, 1959. "Photocontrol of vegetative growth," pp. 129–135 in R. B. Withrow (ed.), *Photoperiodism and related phenomena in plants and animals*, Washington, D.C.: American Association for the Advancement of Science.

————, PIRINGER, A. A., and WIEBE, G. A., 1959. "Effects of photoperiod and kind of supplemental light on growth and reproduction of several varieties of wheat and barley," *Bot. Gaz.*, **120**: 170–177.

DYER, H. J., SKOK, J., and SCULLY, N. J., 1959. "Photoperiodic behavior of sunflower," *Bot. Gaz.*, **121**: 50–55.

EGUCHI, T., MATSUMURA, T., and ASHIZAWA, M., 1958. "The effect of nutrition on flower formation in vegetable crops," *Proc. Am. Soc. Hort. Sci.,* **72:** 343–352.

EL HINNAWY, E. I., 1956. "Some aspects of mineral nutrition and flowering," *Med. Landbouwhogeschool Wageningen,* **56:** 1–51. [*Biol. Abst.,* **32:** 17486 (1958).]

ELLIOTT, B. B., and LEOPOLD, A. C., 1952. "A relationship between photoperiodism and respiration," *Plant Physiol.,* **27:** 787–793.

ENGELMANN, W., 1960. "Endogene Rhythmik und photoperiodische Blühinduktion bei Kalanchoë," *Planta,* **55:** 496–511.

ESAU, K., 1953. *Plant anatomy,* New York: John Wiley and Sons, xii + 735 pp.

——, CURRIER, H. B., and CHEADLE, V., 1957. "Physiology of phloem," *Ann. Rev. Plant Physiol.,* **8:** 349–374.

EVANS, L. T., 1959. "Flower initiation in *Trifolium subterraneum* L. I. Analysis of the partial processes involved," *Austral. J. Agric. Res.,* **10:** 1–16.

——, 1960. "Inflorescence initiation in *Lolium temulentum* L. I. Effect of plant age and leaf area on sensitivity to photoperiodic induction," *Austral. J. Biol. Sci.,* **13:** 123–131.

FINN, J. C., JR., and HAMNER, K. C., 1960. "Investigation of *Hyoscyamus niger* L., a long-day plant, for endodiurnal periodicity in flowering response," *Plant Physiol.,* **35:** 982–985.

FISHER, J. E., 1957. "Effect of gravity on flowering of soybeans," *Science,* **125:** 396.

FLINT, L. H., and MCALISTER, E. D., 1935. "Wavelengths of radiation in the visible spectrum inhibiting the germination of light-sensitive lettuce seed," Smithsonian Misc. Coll. 94 (No. 5), pp. 1–11.

——, ——, 1937. "Wavelengths of radiation in the visible spectrum promoting the germination of light-sensitive lettuce seed," Smithsonian Misc. Coll. 96 (No. 2), pp. 1–8.

FOSTER, A. S., and GIFFORD, E. M., JR., 1959. *Comparative morphology of vascular plants,* San Francisco: W. H. Freeman and Co., xii + 555 pp.

FOX, J. E., and MILLER, C. O., 1959. "Factors in corn steep water promoting growth of plant tissues," *Plant Physiol.,* **34:** 577–579.

FRASER, D. A., 1958. "The relation of environmental factors to flowering in spruce," pp. 629–642 in K. V. Thimann (ed.), *The physiology of forest trees,* New York: Ronald Press.

FULLER, H. J., 1949. "Photoperiodic responses of *Chenopodium quinoa* Willd. and *Amaranthus caudatus* L.," *Am. J. Bot.,* **36:** 175–180.

FUNKE, G. L., 1948. "The photoperiodicity of flowering under short day with supplemental light of different wavelengths," pp. 79–82 in A. E. Murneek and R. O. Whyte (eds.), *Vernalization and photoperiodism,* Waltham, Mass.: Chronica Botanica.

FURR, J. R., and ARMSTRONG, W. W., 1956. "Flower induction in marsh grapefruit in the Coachella Valley, California," *Proc. Am. Soc. Hort. Sci.,* **67:** 176–182.

——, COOPER, W. C., and REECE, P. C., 1947. "An investigation of flower formation in adult and juvenile citrus trees," *Am. J. Bot.,* **34:** 1–8.

Galston, A. W., and Kaur, R., 1961. "Comparative studies on the growth and light sensitivity of green and etiolated pea stem sections," pp. 687–705 in W. D. McElroy and B. Glass (eds.), *Light and Life*, Baltimore: Johns Hopkins Press.

Galun, E., 1959. "Effects of gibberellic acid and naphthaleneacetic acid on sex expression and some morphological characters in the cucumber plant," *φyton* (Argentina), 13: 1–8.

Gardner, F. P., and Loomis, W. E., 1953. "Floral induction and development in orchard grass," *Plant Physiol.*, 28: 201–217.

Garner, W. W., and Allard, H. A., 1920. "Effect of the relative length of day and night and other factors of the environment on growth and reproduction in plants," *J. Agric. Res.*, 18: 553–606.

———, ———, 1923. "Further studies in photoperiodism, the response of the plant to relative length of day and night," *J. Agric. Res.*, 23: 871–920.

———, ———, 1925. "Localization of the response in plants to relative length of day and night," *J. Agric. Res.*, 31: 555–566.

Gentscheff, G., and Gustaffson, Å., 1940. "The cultivation of plant species from seed to flower and seed in different agar solutions," *Hereditas*, 26: 250–256.

Gessner, F., 1960. "Die Blütenöffnung der *Victoria regia* in ihrer Beziehung zum Licht," *Planta*, 54: 453–465.

Gott, M. B., Gregory, F. G., and Purvis, O. N., 1955. "Studies in vernalization of cereals. XIII. Photoperiodic control of stages in flowering between initiation and ear formation in vernalized and unvernalized Petkus winter rye," *Ann. Bot.*, n.s., 19: 87–126.

Gowing, D. P., 1956. "An hypothesis of the role of naphthaleneacetic acid in flower induction in the pineapple," *Am. J. Bot.*, 43: 411–418.

Grainger, J. 1939. "Studies upon the time of flowering of plants. Anatomical, floristic, and phenological aspects of the problem," *Ann. Appl. Biol.* (London), 26: 684–704.

Gregory, F. G., and DeRopp, R. S., 1938. "Vernalization of excised embryos," *Nature*, 142: 481–482.

———, and Purvis, O. N., 1938a. "Studies in vernalisation of cereals. II. The vernalisation of excised mature embryos, and of developing ears," *Ann. Bot.*, n.s., 2: 237–251.

———, ———, 1938b. "Studies in vernalisation of cereals. III. The use of anaerobic conditions in the analysis of the vernalising effect of low temperature during germination," *Ann. Bot.*, n.s., 2: 753–764.

Greulach, V. A., and Haesloop, J. G., 1958. "Influence of gibberellin on *Xanthium* flowering as related to number of photoinductive cycles," *Science*, 127: 646–647.

Gulich, L., 1960. "Veränderungen in der Nucleinsäurefraktion grüner Blätter im Zusammenhang mit photoperiodischer Induktion," *Planta*, 54: 374–393.

Guttridge, C. G., 1958. "The effects of winter chilling on the subsequent growth and development of the cultivated strawberry plant," *J. Hort. Sci.*, 33: 119–127.

GUTTRIDGE, C. G., 1959. "Evidence for a flower inhibitor and vegetative growth promoter in the strawberry," *Ann. Bot.*, n.s., **23:** 351–360.

HAMNER, K. C., 1940. "Interrelation of light and darkness in photoperiodic induction," *Bot. Gaz.*, **101:** 658–687.

———, and BONNER, J., 1938. "Photoperiodism in relation to hormones as factors in floral initiation and development," *Bot. Gaz.*, **100:** 388–431.

———, and NANDA, K. K., 1956. "A relationship between applications of indole-acetic acid and the high-intensity-light reaction of photoperiodism," *Bot. Gaz.*, **118:** 13–18.

HARADA, H., and NITSCH, J. P., 1959a. "Changes in endogenous growth substances during flower development," *Plant Physiol.*, **34:** 409–415.

———, ———, 1959b. "Flower induction in Japanese *Chrysanthemum* with gibberellic acid," *Science*, **129:** 777–778.

HARDER, R., 1948. "Vegetative and reproductive development of *Kalanchoë blossfeldiana* as influenced by photoperiodism," *Symp. Soc. Exptl. Biol.*, **2:** 117–138.

———, and BÜNSOW, R., 1954. "Über die Wirkung der Tageslänge vor der Kurztaginduktion auf die Blütenbildung von *Kalanchoë blossfeldiana*," *Planta*, **43:** 315–324.

———, ———, 1956. "Einfluss des Gibberellins auf die Blütenbildung bei *Kalanchoë blossfeldiana*," *Naturwiss.*, **43:** 544.

———, ———, 1957. "Zusammenwirken von Gibberellin mit photoperiodisch bedingten blühfördernden und blühhemmenden Vorgängen bei *Kalanchoë blossfeldiana*," *Naturwiss.*, **44:** 454.

HARTMANN, H. T., 1947. "Some effects of temperature and photoperiod on flower formation and runner production in the strawberry," *Plant Physiol.*, **22:** 407–420.

HAUPT, W., 1958. "Die Blütenbildung bei *Pisum sativum*," *Zeit. Bot.*, **46:** 242–256.

HENDRICKS, S. B., 1958. "Photoperiodism," *Agron. J.*, **50:** 724–729.

———, 1959. "The photoreaction and associated changes of plant photomorpho-genesis," pp. 423–438 in R. B. Withrow (ed.), *Photoperiodism and related phenomena in plants and animals*, Washington, D.C.: American Association for the Advancement of Science.

HESLOP-HARRISON, J., 1957. "The experimental modification of sex expression in flowering plants," *Biol. Revs.*, **32:** 38–90.

———, 1958. "The unisexual flower—a reply to criticism," *Phytomorphol.*, **8:** 177–184.

———, 1960. "Suppressive effect of 2-thiouracil on differentiation and flowering in *Cannabis sativa*," *Science*, **132:** 1943–1944.

———, and HESLOP-HARRISON, Y., 1957. "The effect of carbon monoxide on sexuality in *Mercurialis ambigua* L. fils," *New Phytol.*, **56:** 352–355.

———, ———, 1958a. "Photoperiod, auxin, and sex balance in a long-day plant," *Nature*, **181:** 100–102.

———, ———, 1958b. "Long-day and auxin induced male sterility in *Silene pendula* L.," *Port. Acta Biol., Ser. A*, **5:** 79–94.

HESLOP-HARRISON, J., and HESLOP-HARRISON, Y., 1958c. "Studies on flowering-plant growth and organogenesis. III. Leaf shape changes associated with flowering and sex differentiation in *Cannabis sativa*," *Proc. Roy. Irish Acad., Ser. B*, 59: 257–283.

HESS, D., 1959. "Die selektive Blockierung eines an der Blühinduktion beteiligten Ribosenucleinsäure-eiweissystems durch 2-Thiouracil (Untersuchungen an *Streptocarpus wendlandii*)," *Planta*, 54: 74–94.

HIGHKIN, H. R., 1955. "Flower-promoting activity of pea seed diffusates," *Plant Physiol.*, 30: 390.

⸻, 1956. "Vernalization in peas," *Plant Physiol.*, 31: 399–403.

HILLMAN, W. S., 1959a. "Experimental control of flowering in *Lemna*. I. General methods. Photoperiodism in *L. perpusilla* 6746," *Am. J. Bot.*, 46: 466–473.

⸻, 1959b. "Experimental control of flowering in *Lemna*. II. Some effects of medium composition, chelating agents, and high temperatures on flowering in *L. perpusilla* 6746," *Am. J. Bot.*, 46: 489–495.

⸻, 1959c. "Interaction of growth substances and photoperiodically active radiations on the growth of pea internode sections," pp. 181–196 in R. B. Withrow (ed.), *Photoperiodism and related phenomena in plants and animals*, Washington, D.C.: American Association for the Advancement of Science.

⸻, 1960. "Effects of gibberellic acid on flowering, frond size, and multiplication rate of *Lemna perpusilla*," *φyton* (Argentina), 14: 49–54.

⸻, 1961a. "Photoperiodism, chelating agents, and flowering of *Lemna perpusilla* and *L. gibba* in aseptic culture," pp. 673–686 in W. D. McElroy and B. Glass (eds.), *Light and Life*, Baltimore: Johns Hopkins Press.

⸻, 1961b. "Experimental control of flowering in *Lemna*. III. A relationship between medium composition and the opposite photoperiodic responses of *L. perpusilla* 6746 and *L. gibba* G3," *Am. J. Bot.*, 48: 413–419.

⸻, 1961c. "Heavy metals and the photoperiodic control of flowering in *Lemna*," *Abstr. in Plant Physiol. 36 (Supplement)*, p. liii.

⸻, and GALSTON, A. W., 1961. "The effect of external factors on auxin content," in *Encyclopedia of plant physiology*, Vol. 14, Heidelberg: Springer-Verlag.

HOEKSTRA, P. E., and MERGEN, F., 1957. "Experimental induction of female flowers on young slash pine," *J. Forestry*, 55: 827–831.

HOLDSWORTH, M., 1956. "The concept of minimum leaf number," *J. Exptl. Bot.*, 7: 395–409.

HOLLAENDER, A. (ed.), 1956. *Radiation biology*, Vol. III. *Visible and near-visible light*, New York: McGraw-Hill, viii + 766 pp.

HUBER, B., 1952. "Tree physiology," *Ann. Rev. Plant Physiol.*, 3: 333–346.

HUSSEY, G., 1954. "Experiments with two long-day plants designed to test Bünning's theory of photoperiodism," *Physiol. Plantarum*, 7: 253–260.

HUXLEY, J., 1949. *Soviet genetics and world science. Lysenko and the meaning of heredity*, London: Chatto and Windus, x + 245 pp.

IMAMURA, S., and TAKIMOTO, A., 1955a. "Photoperiodic responses in Japanese morning glory, *Pharbitis nil* Chois., a sensitive short-day plant," *Bot. Mag.* (Tokyo), 68: 235–241.

IMAMURA, S., and TAKIMOTO, A., 1955b. "Transmission rate of photoperiodic stimulus in *Pharbitis nil*," *Bot. Mag.* (Tokyo), **68**: 260–266.

———, ———, 1957. "Effect of ringing and incision given to the stem on the transmission of photoperiodic stimulus in *Pharbitis nil*," *Bot. Mag.* (Tokyo), **70**: 13–16.

JENNINGS, P. R., and ZUCK, R. K., 1954. "The cotyledon in relation to photoperiodism in cocklebur," *Bot. Gaz.*, **116**: 199–200.

JUNGES, W., 1958. "Die Wirkung von Tageslänge und Lichtintensität in der Präthermophase bienner Pflanzen," *Ber. Deutsch. Bot. Ges.*, **71**: 197–204.

KANDELER, R., 1955. "Über die Blütenbildung bei *Lemna gibba* L. I. Kulturbedingungen und Tageslängenabhängigkeit," *Zeit. Bot.*, **43**: 61–71.

KHUDAIRI, A.-K., and HAMNER, K. C., 1954a. "The relative sensitivity of *Xanthium* leaves of different ages to photoperiodic induction," *Plant Physiol.*, **29**: 251–257.

———, ———, 1954b. "Effect of ethylene chlorohydrin on floral initiation in *Xanthium*," *Bot. Gaz.*, **115**: 289–291.

KLEBS, G., 1918. "Über die Blütenbildung bei *Sempervivum*," *Flora*, **11–12**: 128–151.

KOHL, H. C., JR., 1958. "Flower initiation of stocks grown with several temperature regimens," *Proc. Am. Soc. Hort. Sci.*, **72**: 481–484.

KOJIMA, H., and MAEDA, M., 1958. "Promotion of flower initiation by restraining the vegetative growth in the Japanese radish," *Bot. Mag.* (Tokyo), **71**: 246–253.

KOLLER, D., HIGHKIN, H. R., and CASO, O. H., 1960. "Effects of gibberellic acid on stem apices of vernalizable grasses," *Am. J. Bot.*, **47**: 518–524.

KONISHI, M., 1956. "Studies on development of flowering stalks in long-day plants in relation to auxin metabolism," Mem. Coll. Agric., Kyoto University, No. 75 (Bot. Ser. No. 3), 70 pp.

KÖNITZ, W., 1958. "Blühhemmung bei Kurztagpflanzen durch Hellrot- und Dunkelrotlicht in der photo- und skotophilen Phase," *Planta*, **51**: 1–29.

KRAUS, E. J., 1925. "Soil nutrients in relation to vegetation and reproduction," *Am. J. Bot.*, **12**: 510–516.

———, and KRAYBILL, H., 1918. "Vegetation and reproduction with special reference to the tomato," Oreg. Agric. Exptl. Sta. Bull. No. 149. Quoted in E. J. Kraus, "Soil nutrients in relation to vegetation and reproduction," *Am. J. Bot.*, **12**: 510–516.

KRIBBEN, F. J., 1955. "Zu den Theorien des Photoperiodismus," *Beitr. Biol. Pflanzen.*, **31**: 297–311.

KRUMWIEDE, D., 1960. "Über die Wirkung von Stark und Schwachlichtkombinationen auf das Blühen von *Kalanchoë blossfeldiana*," *Biol. Zentralbl.*, **79**: 257–278.

KUNITAKE, G. M., SALTMAN, P., and LANG, A., 1957. "The products of CO_2 dark fixation in leaves of long- and short-day treated *Kalanchoë blossfeldiana*," *Plant Physiol.*, **32**: 201–203.

LAIBACH, F., and KRIBBEN, F. J., 1950. "Der Einfluss von Wuchsstoff auf die Bildung männlicher und weiblicher Blüten bei einer monözischen Pflanze (*Cucumis sativus* L.)," *Ber. Deutsch. Bot. Ges.,* **62**: 53–55.

LAM, S. L., and LEOPOLD, A. C., 1960. "Reversion from flowering to the vegetative state in *Xanthium,*" *Am. J. Bot.,* **47**: 256–259.

———, ———, 1961. "Reversion and reinduction of flowering in *Perilla,*" *Am. J. Bot.,* **48**: 306–310.

———, THOMPSON, A. E., and McCOLLUM, J. P., 1959. "Induction of flowering in the sweet potato," *Proc. Am. Soc. Hort. Sci.,* **73**: 453–462.

LANG, A., 1948. "Beiträge zur Genetik des Photoperiodismus. I. Faktorenanalyse des Kurztagcharakters von *Nicotiana tabacum* 'Maryland Mammut.' Nachtrag: Genetik der Vernalisation und des Photoperiodismus," pp. 175–189 in A. E. Murneek and R. O. Whyte (eds.), *Vernalization and photoperiodism,* Waltham, Mass.: Chronica Botanica.

———, 1951. "Untersuchungen über das Kältebedürfnis von zweijährigem *Hyoscyamus niger,*" *Der Züchter,* **21**: 241–243.

———, 1952. "Physiology of flowering," *Ann. Rev. Plant Physiol.,* **3**: 265–306.

———, 1957. "The effect of gibberellin upon flower formation," *Proc. Nat. Acad. Sci.,* **43**: 709–717.

———, 1959. "The influence of gibberellin and auxin on photoperiodic induction," pp. 329–350 in R. B. Withrow (ed.), *Photoperiodism and related phenomena in plants and animals,* Washington, D.C.: American Association for the Advancement of Science.

———, 1960. "Gibberellin-like substances in photoinduced and vegetative *Hyoscyamus* plants," *Planta,* **54**: 498–504.

———, and MELCHERS, G., 1947. "Vernalisation und Devernalisation bei einer zweijährigen Pflanze," *Zeit. Naturf.,* **2b**: 444–449.

———, and REINHARD, E., 1961. "Gibberellins and flower formation," pp. 71–79 in *Advances in chemistry, No. 28,* Washington, D.C.: American Chemical Society.

———, SANDOVAL, J. A., and BEDRI, A., 1957. "Induction of bolting and flowering in *Hyoscyamus* and *Samolus* by a gibberellin-like material from a seed plant," *Proc. Nat. Acad. Sci.,* **43**: 960–964.

LAWRENCE, G. H. M., 1951. *Taxonomy of vascular plants,* New York: Macmillan, xiii + 823 pp.

LEOPOLD, A. C., 1955. *Auxins and plant growth,* Berkeley and Los Angeles: University of California Press, xi + 354 pp.

———, 1958. "Auxin uses in the control of flowering and fruiting," *Ann. Rev. Plant Physiol.,* **9**: 281–310.

———, NIEDERGANG-KAMIEN, E., and JANICK, J., 1959. "Experimental modification of plant senescence," *Plant Physiol.,* **34**: 570–573.

———, and THIMANN, K. V., 1949. "The effect of auxin on flower initiation," *Am. J. Bot.,* **36**: 343–347.

LEWIS, H., and WENT, F. W., 1945. "Plant growth under controlled conditions. IV. Response of California annuals to photoperiod and temperature," *Am. J. Bot.,* **32**: 1–12.

LINCOLN, R. G., and HAMNER, K. C., 1958. "An effect of gibberellic acid on the flowering of *Xanthium*, a short-day plant," *Plant Physiol.*, **33:** 101–104.

——, MAYFIELD, D. L., and CUNNINGHAM, A., 1961. "Preparation of a floral initiating extract from *Xanthium*," *Science*, **133:** 756.

——, RAVEN, K. A., and HAMNER, K. C., 1956. "Certain factors influencing expression of the flowering stimulus in *Xanthium*. Part I. Translocation and inhibition of the flowering stimulus," *Bot. Gaz.*, **117:** 193–206.

——, ——, ——, 1958. "Certain factors influencing expression of the flowering stimulus in *Xanthium*. Part II. Relative contribution of buds and leaves to effectiveness of inductive treatment," *Bot. Gaz.*, **119:** 179–185.

LIVERMAN, J. L., 1955. "The physiology of flowering," *Ann. Rev. Plant Physiol.*, **6:** 177–210.

——, and LANG, A., 1956. "Induction of flowering in long-day plants by applied indoleacetic acid," *Plant Physiol.*, **31:** 147–150.

LOCKHART, J. A., and HAMNER, K. C., 1954. "Partial reactions in the formation of the floral stimulus in *Xanthium*," *Plant Physiol.*, **29:** 509–513.

LONA, F., 1956. "Osservazioni orientative circa l'effetto dell'acido gibberellico sullo sviluppo riproduttivo di alcune longidiurne e brevidiurne," *L'Ateneo Parmense*, **27:** 867–875.

——, 1959. "Results of twelve years of work on the photoperiodic responses of *Perilla ocymoides*," *Koninkl. Ned. Akad. Wet., Proc.*, **C62:** 204–210.

LONG, E. M., 1939. "Photoperiodic induction as influenced by environmental factors," *Bot. Gaz.*, **101:** 168–188.

LONGMAN, K. A., and WAREING, P. F., 1958. "Effect of gravity on flowering and shoot growth in Japanese larch (*Larix leptolepis*, Murray)," *Nature*, **182:** 380–381.

——, ——, 1959. "Early induction of flowering in birch seedlings," *Nature*, **184:** 2037–2038.

LÖVE, A., and LÖVE, D., 1945. "Experiments on the effects of animal sex hormones on dioecious plants," *Ark. Bot.*, **32A:** 1–60.

MANN, L. K., 1940. "Effect of some environmental factors on floral initiation in *Xanthium*," *Bot. Gaz.*, **102:** 339–356.

McCLURE, F. A., and KENNARD, W. A., 1955. "Propagation of bamboo by whole-culm cuttings," *Proc. Am. Soc. Hort. Sci.*, **65:** 283–288.

McKINNEY, H. H., 1940. "Vernalization and the growth-phase concept," *Bot. Rev.*, **6:** 25–47.

MEIJER, G., 1959. "The spectral dependence of flowering and elongation," *Acta Bot. Neerl.*, **8:** 189–246.

MELCHERS, G., 1956. "Die Beteiligung der endonomen Tagesrhythmik am Zustandebekommen der photoperiodischen Reaktion der Kurztagpflanze *Kalanchoë blossfeldiana*," *Zeit. Naturf.*, **11b:** 544–548.

——, and LANG, A., 1948. "Die Physiologie der Blütenbildung," *Biol. Zentralbl.*, **67:** 105–164.

MILLER, C., and SKOOG, F., 1953. "Chemical control of bud formation in tobacco stem segments," *Am. J. Bot.*, **40:** 768–773.

MIROV, N. T., 1956. "Photoperiod and flowering of pines," *Forest Sci.,* **2:** 328–332.

———, and STANLEY, R. G., 1959. "The pine tree," *Ann. Rev. Plant Physiol.,* **10:** 223–238.

MOORE, T. C., and BONDE, E. K., 1958. "Interaction of gibberellic acid and vernalization in the dwarf telephone pea," *Physiol. Plantarum,* **11:** 752–759.

MOSHKOV, B. S., 1939. "Transfer of photoperiodic reaction from leaves to growing points," *C. R. (Doklady) Acad. Sci. U.R.S.S.,* **24:** 489–491.

MURNEEK, A. E., 1940. "Length of day and temperature effects in *Rudbeckia,*" *Bot. Gaz.,* **102:** 269–279.

———, and WHYTE, R. O., (eds.), 1948. *Vernalization and photoperiodism* (Lotsya No. 1), Waltham, Mass.: Chronica Botanica, xv + 196 pp.

NAKAYAMA, S., 1958. "Studies on the dark process in the photoperiodic response of *Pharbitis* seedlings," *The Science Reports of the Tohoku University, 4th Series, Biology,* **24:** 137–183.

———, BORTHWICK, H. A., and HENDRICKS, S. B., 1960. "Failure of photoreversible control of flowering in *Pharbitis nil,*" *Bot. Gaz.,* **121:** 237–243.

———, and KIKUCHI, T., 1956. "Experimental researches on photoperiodism (4). The effect of auxin application on flower formation," *Miyazaki University Bull., Fac. Lib. Arts and Ed.,* **1:** 154–165.

NANDA, K. K., and HAMNER, K. C., 1958. "Studies on the nature of the endogenous rhythm affecting photoperiodic response of Biloxi soybean," *Bot. Gaz.,* **120:** 14–25.

———, ———, 1959. "Photoperiodic cycles of different lengths in relation to flowering in Biloxi soybean (*Glycine max* L.; Merr.)," *Planta,* **53:** 45–52.

NAPP-ZINN, K., 1960. "Vernalisation, Licht und Alter bei *Arabidopsis thaliana* (L.) Heynh. I. Licht und Dunkelheit während Kälte- und Wärmebehandlung," *Planta,* **54:** 409–444.

NAYLOR, A. W., 1941. "Effects of some environmental factors on photoperiodic induction of beet and dill," *Bot. Gaz.,* **102:** 557–575.

———, 1953. "Reactions of plants to photoperiod," pp. 149–178 in W. E. Loomis (ed.), *Growth and differentiation in plants,* Ames: Iowa State University Press.

NAYLOR, F. L., 1941. "Effect of length of induction period on floral development of *Xanthium pennsylvanicum,*" *Bot. Gaz.,* **103:** 146–154.

NITSCH, J. P., 1957. "Photoperiodism in woody plants," *Proc. Am. Soc. Hort. Sci.,* **70:** 526–544.

———, and HARADA, H., 1958. "Production de fleurs en jours courts par l'alcool furfurylique chez le *Rudbeckia speciosa,*" *Bull. Soc. Bot. Fr.,* **105:** 319–322.

———, KURTZ, E. B., JR., LIVERMAN, J. L., and WENT, F. W., 1952. "The development of sex expression in cucurbit flowers," *Am. J. Bot.,* **39:** 32–43.

——— and WENT, F. W., 1959. "The induction of flowering in *Xanthium pennsylvanicum* under long days," in R. B. Withrow (ed.), *Photoperiodism and related phenomena in plants and animals,* Washington, D.C.: American Association for the Advancement of Science.

OEHLKERS, F., 1956. "Veränderungen in der Blühbereitschaft vernalisierter Cotyledonen von *Streptocarpus*, kenntlich gemacht durch Blattstecklinge," *Zeit. Naturf.*, **11b:** 471–480.

OGAWA, Y., 1960. "Über die Auslösung der Blütenbildung von *Pharbitis nil* durch niedere Temperatur," *Bot. Mag.* (Tokyo), **73:** 334–335.

OKUDA, M., 1953. "Flower formation of *Xanthium canadense* under long-day conditions induced by grafting with long-day plants," *Bot. Mag.* (Tokyo), **66:** 247–255.

OLTMANNS, O., 1960. "Über den Einfluss der Temperatur auf die endogene Tagesrhythmik und die Blühinduktion bei der Kurztagpflanze *Kalanchoë blossfeldiana*," *Planta*, **54:** 233–264.

OVERLAND, L., 1960. "Endogenous rhythm in opening and odor of flowers of *Cestrum nocturnum*," *Am. J. Bot.*, **47:** 378–382.

PATON, D. M., and BARBER, H. N., 1955. "Physiological genetics in *Pisum*. I. Grafting experiments between early and late varieties," *Austral. J. Biol. Sci.*, **8:** 231–240.

PETERSON, C. E., and ANHDER, L. D., 1960. "Induction of staminate flowers on gynoecious cucumbers with gibberellin A_3," *Science*, **131:** 1673–1674.

PHILIPSON, W. R., 1949. "The ontogeny of the shoot apex in dicotyledons," *Biol. Revs.*, **24:** 21–50.

PHINNEY, B. O., and WEST, C. A., 1960. "Gibberellins as native plant growth regulators," *Ann. Rev. Plant Physiol.*, **11:** 411–436.

PIRINGER, A. A., and BORTHWICK, H. A., 1955. "Photoperiodic responses of coffee," *Turrialba*, **5:** 72–77.

———, and DOWNS, R. J., 1959. "Responses of apple and peach trees to various photoperiods," *Proc. Am. Soc. Hort. Sci.*, **73:** 9–15.

PITTENDRIGH, C. S., and BRUCE, V. G., 1959. "Daily rhythms as coupled oscillator systems and their relation to thermoperiodism and photoperiodism," pp. 475–505 in R. B. Withrow (ed.), *Photoperiodism and related phenomena in plants and animals*, Washington, D.C.: American Association for the Advancement of Science.

Plant growth regulation, 1961. Ames: Iowa State University Press, xiv + 850 pp.

PURVIS, O. N., 1934. "An analysis of the influence of temperature during germination on the subsequent development of certain winter cereals and its relation to the effect of length of day," *Ann. Bot.*, **48:** 917–955.

———, 1939. "Studies in vernalisation of cereals. V. The inheritance of the spring and winter habit in hybrids of Petkus rye," *Ann. Bot.*, n.s., **3:** 719–729.

———, 1940. "Vernalisation of fragments of embryo tissue," *Nature*, **145:** 462.

———, 1960. "Effect of gibberellin on the flower initiation and stem extension in Petkus winter rye," *Nature*, **185:** 479.

———, and GREGORY, F. G., 1937. "Studies in vernalisation of cereals. I. A comparative study of vernalisation of winter rye by low temperature and by short days," *Ann. Bot.*, n.s., **1:** 569–591.

RESENDE, F., 1959. "On the transmission of the 'floral state,' through grafting, from LSDP or SDP-donors to LSDP-acceptors in LD and SD," *Port. Acta Biol., Ser. A,* **6:** 1–17.

RICHARDS, P. W., 1957. *The tropical rain forest: An ecological study,* Cambridge: Cambridge University Press, xviii + 450 pp.

ROBBINS, W. J., 1957. "Gibberellic acid and the reversal of adult *Hedera* to a juvenile state," *Am. J. Bot.,* **44:** 743–746.

———, 1960. "Further observations on juvenile and adult *Hedera,*" *Am. J. Bot.,* **47:** 485–491.

ROBERTS, R. H., 1951. "The induction of flowering with a plant extract," pp. 347–350 in F. Skoog (ed.), *Plant growth substances,* Madison: University of Wisconsin Press.

———, and STRUCKMEYER, B. E., 1938. "The effects of temperature and other environmental factors upon the photoperiodic responses of some of the higher plants," *J. Agric. Res.,* **56:** 633–677.

SACHS, J., 1887. "Über die Wirkung der ultravioletten Strahlen auf die Blütenbildung," *Arb. Bot. Inst. Würzburg,* **3:** 372.

SACHS, R. M., 1959. "Dual daylength requirements for floral initiation," pp. 315–319 in R. B. Withrow (ed.), *Photoperiodism and related phenomena in plants and animals,* Washington, D.C.: American Association for the Advancement of Science.

———, BRETZ, C. F., and LANG, A., 1959. "Shoot histogenesis: The early effects of gibberellin upon stem elongation in two rosette plants," *Am. J. Bot.,* **46:** 376–384.

———, LANG, A., BRETZ, C. F., and ROACH, J., 1960. "Shoot histogenesis: Subapical meristematic activity in a caulescent plant and the action of gibberellic acid and Amo-1618," *Am. J. Bot.,* **47:** 260–266.

SALISBURY, F. B., 1955. "The dual role of auxin in flowering," *Plant Physiol.,* **30:** 327–334.

———, and BONNER, J., 1960. "Inhibition of photoperiodic induction by 5-fluorouracil," *Plant Physiol.,* **35:** 173–177.

SARKAR, S., 1958. "Versuche zur Physiologie der Vernalisation," *Biol. Zentralbl.,* **77:** 1–49.

SAX, K., 1957. "The control of vegetative growth and the induction of early fruiting of apple trees," *Proc. Am. Soc. Hort. Sci.,* **69:** 68–74.

———, 1958a. "The juvenile characters of trees and shrubs," *Arnoldia,* **18:** 1–6.

———, 1958b. "Experimental control of tree growth and reproduction," pp. 601–610 in K. V. Thimann (ed.), *The physiology of forest trees,* New York: Ronald Press.

SCHMITZ, J., 1951. "Über Beziehungen zwischen Blütenbildung in verschiedenen Licht-Dunkelkombinationen und Atmungsrhythmik bei wechselnden photoperiodischen Bedingungen," *Planta,* **39:** 271–308.

SCHWABE, W. W., 1950. "Factors controlling flowering of the chrysanthemum. I. The effects of photoperiod and temporary chilling," *J. Exptl. Bot.,* **1:** 329–343.

SCHWABE, W. W., 1954. "Factors controlling flowering in the chrysanthemum. IV. The site of vernalization and translocation of the stimulus," *J. Exptl. Bot.*, **5**: 389–400.

———, 1955a. "Photoperiodic cycles of lengths differing from 24 hours in relation to endogenous rhythms," *Physiol. Plantarum*, **8**: 263–278.

———, 1955b. "Factors controlling flowering in the chrysanthemum. V. Devernalization in relation to high temperature and low light intensity treatments," *J. Exptl. Bot.*, **6**: 435–450.

———, 1957. "Factors controlling flowering in the chrysanthemum. VI. Devernalization by low light intensity in relation to temperature and carbohydrate supply," *J. Exptl. Bot.*, **8**: 220–234.

———, 1959. "Studies of long-day inhibition in short-day plants," *J. Exptl. Bot.*, **10**: 317–329.

SCHWEMMLE, B., 1957. "Zur Temperaturabhängigkeit der Blütenbildung und der endogenen Tagesrhythmik bei *Kalanchoë blossfeldiana*," *Naturwiss.*, **44**: 356.

———, 1960. "Unterschiedliche Schwankungen der Temperaturempfindlichkeit bei Lang- und Kurztagpflanzen (Versuche zur Blütenbildung)," *Naturwiss.*, **47**: 68–69.

SHIBATA, O., 1959. "Photoperiodic response of the rice plant as affected by iron deficiency," *Bot. Mag.* (Tokyo), **72**: 477.

SINNOTT, E. W., 1960. *Plant morphogenesis*, New York: McGraw-Hill, x + 550 pp.

SIRONVAL, C., 1957. "La photopériode et la sexualisation du fraisier des quatre-saisons à fruits rouges," C. R. de Recherches-Trav. Cen. Rech. des Hormones Végétales (1952–1956), I.R.S.I.A., Bruxelles, Belgium.

SKOOG, F., and TSUI, C., 1948. "Chemical control of growth and bud formation in tobacco stem segments and callus cultured in vitro," *Am. J. Bot.*, **35**: 782–787.

SMITH, H. J., MCILRATH, W. J., and BOGORAD, L., 1957. "Some effects of iron deficiency on flowering of *Xanthium*," *Bot. Gaz.*, **118**: 174–179.

SNYDER, W. E., 1948. "Mechanism of the photoperiodic response of *Plantago lanceolata* L., a long-day plant," *Am. J. Bot.*, **35**: 520–525.

STANLEY, R. G., 1958. "Methods and concepts applied to a study of flowering in pine," pp. 583–599 in K. V. Thimann, *The physiology of forest trees*, New York: Ronald Press.

STEIN, D. B., and STEIN, O. L., 1960. "The growth of the stem tip of *Kalanchoë* cv. 'Brilliant Star,' " *Am. J. Bot.*, **47**: 132–140.

STOLWIJK, J. A. J., and ZEEVART, J. A. D., 1955. "Wavelength dependence of different light reactions governing flowering in *Hyoscyamus niger*," *Koninkl. Ned. Akad. Wet., Proc.*, **C58**: 386–396.

STOUT, M., 1945. "Translocation of the reproductive stimulus in sugar beets," *Bot. Gaz.*, **107**: 86–95.

STOWE, B. B., and YAMAKI, T., 1957. "The history and physiological action of the gibberellins," *Ann. Rev. Plant Physiol.*, **8**: 181–216.

———, ———, 1960. "Gibberellins: stimulants of plant growth," *Science*, **129**: 807–816.

156 · Bibliography

STRUCKMEYER, B. E., and ROBERTS, R. H., 1955. "The inhibition of abnormal cell proliferation with antiauxin," *Am. J. Bot.,* **42**: 401–405.

TAKIMOTO, A., 1955. "Flowering response to various combinations of light and dark periods in *Silene armeria,*" *Bot. Mag.* (Tokyo), **68**: 308–314.

THIMANN, K. V. (ed.), 1958. *The physiology of forest trees,* New York: Ronald Press, xiv + 678 pp.

THOMPSON, H. C., 1953. "Vernalization of growing plants," pp. 179–196 in W. E. Loomis (ed.), *Growth and differentiation in plants,* Ames: Iowa State College Press.

THOMPSON, P. A., and GUTTRIDGE, C. G., 1959. "Effect of gibberellic acid on the initiation of flowers and runners in the strawberry," *Nature,* **184**: (B.A.): 72–73.

TUCKER, S. C., 1960. "Ontogeny of the floral apex of *Michelia fuscata,*" *Am. J. Bot.,* **47**: 266–277.

VAARTAJA, O., 1959. "Evidence of photoperiodic ecotypes in trees," *Ecol. Monographs,* **29**: 91–111.

VAN DER VEEN, R., and MEIJER, G., 1959. *Light and plant growth,* New York: Macmillan, 162 pp.

VAN OVERBEEK, J., 1952. "Agricultural application of growth regulators and their physiological basis," *Ann. Rev. Plant Physiol.,* **3**: 87–108.

———, and CRUZADO, H. J., 1948. "Flower formation in the pineapple plant by geotropic stimulation," *Am. J. Bot.,* **35**: 410–412.

VLITOS, A. J., and MEUDT, W., 1954. "The role of auxin in plant flowering. III. Free indole acids in short-day plants grown under photoinductive and nonphotoinductive daylengths," *Contr. Boyce-Thompson Inst.,* **17**: 413–417.

———, ———, 1955. "Interactions between vernalization and photoperiod in spinach," *Contr. Boyce Thompson Inst.,* **18**: 159–166.

VON DENFFER, D., 1950. "Blühormon oder Blühemmung? Neue Gesichtspunkte sur Physiologie der Blütenbildung," *Naturwiss.,* **37**: 296–301; 317–321.

———, and SCHLITT, L., 1951. "Blühförderung durch Ultraviolettbestrahlung," *Naturwiss.,* **38**: 564–565.

WAREING, P. F., 1954. "Experiments on the 'light-break' effect in short-day plants," *Physiol. Plantarum,* **7**: 157–172.

———, 1956. "Photoperiodism in woody plants," *Ann. Rev. Plant Physiol.,* **7**: 191–214.

———, and NASR, T., 1958. "Effects of gravity on growth, apical dominance, and flowering in fruit trees," *Nature,* **182**: 379–380.

WASSINK, E. C., DELINT, P. J. A. L., and BENSINK, J., 1959. "Some effects of high-intensity irradiation of narrow spectral regions," pp. 111–127 in R. B. Withrow (ed.), *Photoperiodism and related phenomena in plants and animals,* Washington, D.C.: American Association for the Advancement of Science.

———, and STOLWIJK, J. A. J., 1956. "Effects of light quality on plant growth," *Ann. Rev. Plant Physiol.,* **7**: 373–400.

WENT, F. W., 1948. "*Thermoperiodicity*," pp. 145–157 in A. E. Murneek and R. O. Whyte (eds.), *Vernalization and photoperiodism*, Waltham, Mass.: Chronica Botanica.

———, 1953. "The effect of temperature on plant growth," *Ann. Rev. Plant Physiol.*, **4**: 347–362.

———, 1957. *The experimental control of plant growth*, Waltham, Mass.: Chronica Botanica, xii + 343 pp. + 27 plates.

———, 1959. "The periodic aspect of photoperiodism and thermoperiodicity," pp. 551–564 in R. B. Withrow (ed.), *Photoperiodism and related phenomena in plants and animals*, Washington, D.C.: American Association for the Advancement of Science.

WESTERGAARD, M., 1958. "The mechanism of sex determination in dioecious flowering plants," *Adv. Genetics*, **9**: 217–281.

WETMORE, R. H., 1953. "The use of 'in vitro' cultures in the investigation of growth and differentiation in vascular plants," pp. 22–38 in *Abnormal and pathological plant growth*, Brookhaven Symposia in Biology, No. 6, Upton, N.Y.

———, GIFFORD, E. M., JR., and GREEN, M. C., 1959. "Development of vegetative and floral buds," pp. 255–273 in R. B. Withrow (ed.), *Photoperiodism and related phenomena in plants and animals*, Washington, D.C.: American Association for the Advancement of Science.

WHYTE, R. O., 1948. "History of research in vernalization," pp. 1–38 in A. E. Murneek and R. O. Whyte (eds.), *Vernalization and Photoperiodism*, Waltham, Mass.: Chronica Botanica.

WITHROW, A. P., and WITHROW, R. B., 1943. "Translocation of the floral stimulus in *Xanthium*," *Bot. Gaz.*, **104**: 409–416.

WITHROW, R. B., 1959. "A kinetic analysis of photoperiodism," pp. 439–471 in R. B. Withrow (ed.), *Photoperiodism and related phenomena in plants and animals*, Washington, D.C.: American Association for the Advancement of Science.

——— (ed.), 1959. *Photoperiodism and related phenomena in plants and animals*, Washington, D.C.: American Association for the Advancement of Science (Publication No. 55), xvii + 903 pp.

WITTWER, S. H., and BUKOVAC, M. J., 1958. "The effects of gibberellin on economic crops," *Econ. Botany*, **12**: 213–255.

———, and TEUBNER, F. G., 1956. "Cold exposure of tomato seedlings and flower formation," *Proc. Am. Soc. Hort. Sci.*, **67**: 369–376.

———, ———, 1957. "The effects of temperature and nitrogen nutrition on flower formation in the tomato," *Am. J. Bot.*, **44**: 125–129.

YOSHIMURA, F., 1943. "The significance of molybdenum for the growth of Lemnaceae plants," *Bot. Mag.* (Tokyo), **57**: 371–386.

ZABKA, G. G., 1961. "Photoperiodism in *Amaranthus caudatus*. I. A re-examination of the photoperiodic response," *Am. J. Bot.*, **48**: 21–28.

ZEEVAART, J. A. D., 1958. "Flower formation as studied by grafting," *Med. Landbouwhogeschool Wageningen*, **58**: 1–88.

ZIMMERMAN, P. W., and KJENNERUD, J., 1950. "Flowering and other responses induced in *Piqueria trinervia* with photoperiodic treatment," *Contr. Boyce Thompson Inst.*, **16:** 177–189.

ZIRKLE, C., 1949. *Death of a science in Russia; the fate of genetics as described in Pravda and elsewhere,* Philadelphia: University of Pennsylvania Press, xiv + 319 pp.

index of plant names

subject index

Acetylene, 108

Action spectra, *see* Light-breaks; Light quality

Age, and flowering in woody perennials, 120–126; of leaves, and photoperiodism, 117, 119–120; of plants, and response to cold, 118—and photoperiodism, 5, 15–16, 118–120; *see also* Juvenility

Altitude, 90

Annuals, 6, 54, 136

Anthesis, 7, 127–130

Antiauxin, 106–109, 132–133

Auxin, definition, 68; and induction, 89–91; inhibition of flowering, 79, 90–91, 106–108; promotion of flowering, 90, 106–108; and red, far-red system, 91; and sex expression, 132–133; and vernalization, 118; *see also* Antiauxin

Bark inversion, 123–124

Bending, 90–91, 124

Biennials, cold requirements, 54, 58–59, 61–62, 118; definition, 6; genetics of, 135

Bolting, caused by furfuryl alcohol, 109; definition, 101; and gibberellin, 101–104, 137

Bulb plants, 64–66

Carbohydrate, and devernalization, 60–61; -nitrogen ratio, 112, 119; promotion of flowering, 79; substitution for high-intensity light, 21; trans-

location, and florigen translocation, 73–77, 79—and flowering in woody perennials, 123–125; and vernalization, 57

Carbon dioxide, 21–22, 92

Carbon monoxide, 133

Cereals, winter and spring, devernalization of, 59–60; genetics of, 134–135; and gibberellin, 101; minimum leaf number in, 117; vernalization of, 54–57

Chelating agents, 114–115

Chlorophyll, 31–32, 41

Circadian rhythms, *see* Endogenous circadian rhythms

Cold requirements for flowering, of biennials, 54, 58–59, 61–62, 118; in bulb plants, 64–66; genetics of, 134–135; of perennials, 59; and plant age, 118, 135; relation to photoperiodism, 61–62; satisfaction of, by diffusate, 111—by gibberellin, 100–101—by short days, 61–62; of winter annuals, 54–58; *see also* Vernalization

Cold treatments, of bulbs, 64–66; of developed plants, 54, 58–59, 61–64; effects of, on dormancy, 62, 129—on seed germination, 57—on vegetative growth, 59–60, 64; of germinating seeds, 54–58, 62; seasonal control by, 54, 129; *see also* Vernalization

Copper, 115

Cotyledons, 38–39, 119

Critical daylength, definition and qualifications, 13, 15, 20, 22–24; and

161